lc

DATE DUE

FEB 25 '69			
APR 25 '69			
NOV 17 1976			
~~CANCELLED~~ JAN 19 1981			
NOV 2 5 1981			
JAN 1 8 1983			
DEC 1 3 1984			
JAN 2 9 1985			
OCT 3 0 1985			
NOV 15 1985			
MAY 1 8 2015			
GAYLORD			PRINTED IN U.S.A.

FREDERIC EDWIN CHURCH

67. The Andes of Ecuador

FREDERIC EDWIN CHURCH

An Exhibition Organized by the National Collection of Fine Arts
Smithsonian Institution, Washington, D.C.

NATIONAL COLLECTION OF FINE ARTS · *Smithsonian Institution* · *February 12 to March 13, 1966*
ALBANY INSTITUTE OF HISTORY AND ART · *Albany, New York* · *March 30 to April 30, 1966*
M. KNOEDLER AND COMPANY · *New York* · *June 1 to 30, 1966*

Smithsonian publication 4657
Designed by Crimilda Pontes
Produced by The Meriden Gravure Company
and The Anthoensen Press

Cover illustration: *Rainy Season in the Tropics,*
collection of J. W. Middendorf II

FOREWORD

THE EXHIBITION of the work of Frederic Church allows the National Collection of Fine Arts to participate in the very timely review of a central figure in nineteenth-century American landscape painting. We are happy to join with the Albany Institute of History and Art and M. Knoedler and Company of New York City in calling attention to this very able painter at the moment when there is a possibility that his delightful estate, Olana, may become a public monument both to the Hudson River School of painting and to later nineteenth-century eclectic taste in architecture and decoration.

The National Collection, with its concern for advancing the appreciation of American art, is happily privileged to share in the presentation of this exhibition and catalogue. We join with the other exhibitors in expressing our appreciation to the many contributors who have made it possible for us to enjoy a broad view of Church's work for the first time in nearly sixty-six years. We are pleased to acknowledge the

scholarly support of Professor David C. Huntington, the many essential contribu-
tions of Dr. Richard P. Wunder of our staff, the encouragement of Mr. Alexander
Aldrich (President of Olana Preservation, Incorporated), and finally the generosity
and helpfulness of Mr. Christian Rohlfing and the staff of the Cooper Union Museum.

DAVID W. SCOTT
Director
National Collection of Fine Arts

[8]

PREFACE

IT IS TIMELY that in 1966 Frederic Edwin Church (1826-1900), who today is considered the greatest of the so-called Hudson River painters, should be reassessed. His last one-man show was the memorial exhibition staged by the Metropolitan Museum of Art (of which he had been a founding trustee) six weeks following his death in 1900. It consisted of 14 of his major paintings, an important but small segment of his entire oeuvre. It has remained for the present exhibition to represent Church's work fully for the first time.

This exhibition, comprising 43 paintings, 57 oil studies, 81 drawings and sketches, and personal memorabilia, including items relating to the building of Olana, should place Frederic Church more properly in the annals of American painting. It will, hopefully, at the same time bring into clearer focus those characteristics which define this particular phase in the art of landscape painting in the nineteenth century.

What explains the lapse of interest in Church and his art these many years, when so many American artists of his time have enjoyed continued recognition? A key factor is found in the peak years of his career, about 1857-1868. Church's first outstanding success, *Niagara*, in 1857, bringing him international reputation, was eclipsed two years later with *The Heart of the Andes*, which sold for ten thousand dollars, the highest price ever paid to that date for a landscape painting by a living American artist. While he broke exhibition attendance and picture-sale records for a decade thereafter, Church's triumph began to flag by the time he made his trip abroad in 1868. In England he was hailed by Ruskin and other eminent critics of the day as being responsible for producing "an entirely new and higher view both of American nature and art." Immediately following his return home in 1869 he settled down to the pleasurable task of building his oriental castle, Olana, whose situation commands a breathtaking panoramic view of the entire upper Hudson Valley. Perhaps Church elected this way of life to fabricate for himself and his family a romantically comfortable existence, rather orientally opulent. But for the first time a certain feebleness seems to penetrate his art, particularly the larger, more ambitious works. This unfortunate undertone appears in the form of an overly pervasive broadening in the idealization of nature. The details of form are subordinated to the effects of light, and the desire to express the vastness of God's universe overwhelms him. The attention to detail, which had been an obviously joyful concern of the artist previously, was now all but suppressed in order to avoid interfering with the cosmic impact the scene was intended to convey. Yet in his smaller works executed during these later years, Church remained appealingly fresh.

After about 1880 Frederic Church all but ceased serious work, producing only about a half dozen or so finished pictures from that time until his death twenty years later. He apparently realized what was happening to his art and slowed down his activity in order to take stock of himself. In addition he was experiencing the discomfort of seeing his popularity slipping away even during his peak years, due, for the most part, to an undercurrent of change of taste in art in general, over which he had no control, and which led, during the last quarter of the nineteenth century, directly into the so-called modern styles then taking form both in this country and abroad. A critic of an exhibition held at the National Academy of Design welcomed, as early as 1875, "with joy unfeigned an exhibition in which landscape art [held] a somewhat subordinate rank instead of that place of supremacy which was formerly the dread of the ordinary visitor, and which some years [previously] reached a point so absolute that walking through the Academy seemed like exiling oneself among wildernesses where the human form was unknown." The year following another observer noted that "Church and Bierstadt were paid what might well be characterized as 'fabulous prices' ten years ago for pictures that would now sell for a tenth their former market value." At the time Church died the obituary notices stated that "the fact that he was still alive has been almost forgotten by present day artists," and that most of the "rising generation of painters [will] confuse Frederick Edwin Church with Frederick Stuart Church." This is indeed poor commentary on the state of Church's reputation by the year 1900. Critics agreed, however, that Church had "undoubtedly played an important part in the development of American art." Church's fame has thus endured these past sixty-odd years.

At the time of Church's death virtually every oil study, drawing, and sketch remained in his studio at Olana. These sketches, kept to refer to when composing a picture, constituted, as it were, the artist's pictorial reference file. Seventeen years following Church's death, his son and principal heir, Louis Palmer Church, invited the Hewitt sisters, founders of the Cooper Union Museum for the Arts of Decoration, to make a selection from the vast quantities of this material that was now lying unappreciated and unused in the attic at Olana. The Misses Hewitt were eager to acquire examples of artists' work that were shunned by other museums at that time as being too ephemeral to bother with preserving—sketches and drawings, constituting the artists' first creative efforts. They had already accepted for their rapidly growing museum virtually the entire remaining contents of the studio of Winslow Homer. Now, as the result of Louis Church's offer, the Cooper Union Museum acquired some five hundred and fifty oil studies and more than two thousand sketches and larger drawings, comprising about two-thirds of Frederic Church's total legacy in these categories.

As it was Church's habit to cut up his sketchbooks and even some of the larger drawings in order to shuffle them about to fit his needs of the moment, many of the Cooper Union Museum sketches belong in sequence with those still at Olana, and vice versa, thus adding to the art historian's difficulty in reconstituting Church's work in its proper chronological sequence. It is often on the basis of the dates found on these drawings that it has been possible to reconstruct the artist's various trips and movements year by year and month by month.

Until recently the only place where Church could be studied in depth was at the Cooper Union Museum, thanks to the foresight of the Hewitts and Louis Church's generosity. Olana has remained shut up for over a half a century. Its collections, including nearly a hundred finished paintings by Church, many others by his artist-friends, and a group of "Old Masters," were inaccessible except to a very few scholars or close family friends fortunate enough to be invited to visit the house. Now, following the death of Louis Church's widow, the last surviving immediate member of the family, Olana risks being destroyed, the property divided, and the contents of the house and its collections scattered to the four winds. The urgent need at this time is to bring Frederic Edwin Church to the attention of the public. The interest stimulated by the present show could be a major factor in the preservation of this unique segment of our national cultural heritage.

It is appropriate that this exhibition should be shared by a major museum in closest proximity to Olana, the Albany Institute of History and Art, and by M. Knoedler and Company, Church's original dealer. It was at Goupil's Gallery in New York, which later became M. Knoedler and Company, that Church's most important commercial showings were held from the 1860's on.

I should like to express my most sincere thanks to the various private collectors and museums for their willingness to cooperate in every possible way with the assembling of this exhibition. In one instance an exceedingly generous lender preferred giving one of her two paintings by Church to the National Collection of Fine Arts to seeing both lent under her name. To Mrs. Frank R. McCoy I should like to extend this particular expression of gratitude. To Professor David C. Huntington, with whom I have shared happy hours over some dozen years in the study of Church and his art, my heartiest thanks for this pleasurable pursuit. It is through Mr. Huntington's unflagging enthusiasm that the Olana Preservation group has come into being and that the selection of the major works for this show has been possible. Finally, to Dr. David Winfield Scott and my colleagues at the Smithsonian, who have supported the efforts which this exhibition and catalogue have required, my sincerest gratitude is here expressed.

RICHARD P. WUNDER
Curator of Painting and Sculpture
National Collection of Fine Arts   [13]

Frederic Edwin Church (photograph taken in the 1860's)

INTRODUCTION

In the beginning all the world was America.—John Locke

IF THERE EVER WAS a time in the history of the United States when art was harmoniously integrated with the national life that time was surely the glorious era of "Manifest Destiny." In the middle decades of our nineteenth century there developed a peculiar outlook on the world. The romantic love of nature, the legacy of Rousseau, had in this country by the 1840's evolved into a New World cosmology. Bible-bred, science-minded, cultural nationalists regarded themselves as history's "chosen people." They were living in an atmosphere of millennial expectancy; they believed the mystery of the ages was about to be revealed. Science, the study of nature, was disclosing the true meaning of Biblical prophecy. A purposeful Creation had willed America as the setting for the "Second Beginning." A virgin continent had been ordained to effect the regeneration of the world. In this very real and very mythical ter- [15]

ritory, man and nature would return to Eden. The curse of centuries which had afflicted earth and humanity since Adam's fall was about to be lifted. A New Adam was to be born in a New Creation for the Millennium was at hand.

The New World Man must not fail, for geography had delivered an ultimatum to its Elect. *Homo Americanus* had been favored by the Cosmos. He would have to be worthy of Destiny's highest trust. The final reconciliation of man with nature was the imperative of the hour. Emerson called upon the American artist to reveal the hidden spirituality of the universe, to create art worthy of a continent. Never before nor since has the landscape painter known such urgency. He had been asked to play the role of prophet-seer.

It is only against this background that we can recognize the full significance of the paintings which have been brought together in this exhibition. Frederic Edwin Church was the prophet-seer painter of his generation. He was compared to "Moses who looked on God unveiled"; "His canvas lives . . . . His pictures speak their meaning, have an influence, excite feelings." No other American painter of the 1850's and 1860's enjoyed quite the same popular response. His paintings were public events. Indeed, a whole volume could be devoted to the subject of Church's spectators. On one day in 1857 Horace Greeley, George Bancroft, George Ripley, Henry Ward Beecher, and Charles A. Dana were among the many who saw Church's *Niagara*. In 1859 the crowds of visitors to *The Heart of the Andes* at Church's studio were so large that it became necessary to station two policemen on the sidewalk to keep pedestrian traffic moving. And in St. Louis, in 1861, Mark Twain on his third viewing of *The Heart of the Andes* found himself still gasping "to take all the wonder in." Ten years later New Yorkers stood in a "ring six people deep" to contemplate Church's *Jerusalem*, and this went on "for days."

Church's pictures were icons of the cosmic enthusiasms of the hour. *Niagara* caught the "reality" and "spiritual" suggestion of North America's grandest single scene. Before this great New World landscape the spectator could discover himself as a second Noah. In *The Heart of the Andes* Church "condensed the condensation of nature" into a composite of the world itself, as he placed the spectator midway between tropic lowlands and arctic heights. One spectator viewed the painting and beheld "Mt. Sinai"; others "Arcady," "Elysium," "Paradise," "Eden." An admirer exclaimed, "Whenever I look at it, I feel exactly as I did on Easter-Sunday." *The Heart of the Andes* was the image of nature's eternal regeneration. *Jerusalem*, depicting the city as just cleansed by a storm and now transfigured in the dazzling brilliance of a sunburst, is conceived as "a city on a hill" to which the world looks for its redemption.

Church's great public pictures were consistently "revelations" of the physical and metaphysical order and purpose of the Cosmos. *New England Scenery* (1851) is a pristine Yankee Arcadia. *The Andes of Ecuador* (1855) is a new earth perceived by a mind steeped in geology. *Twilight in the Wilderness* (1860) is Church's perfect heroic *mise en scène* of America's archetypal landscape. Trees, forests, hills, water, and clouds enact the mythology of the moment. It is the New World apocalypse. *The Icebergs* (1861) was the painted last word on the elemental life of northern seas. It celebrated man's imminent reconciliation with nature. However a note of irony was injected into the picture just before Church sent it to London. He then introduced a derelict mast, evidently as a salute to England's haunting memory of the mysterious disappearance of Sir John Franklin and his party in the Arctic seas in 1847. A chromolithograph of this lost masterpiece is included in the exhibition.

Cotopaxi (1862), painted early in the Civil War, dramatized the struggle between the forces of darkness and the forces of light. A natural cross which burns upon the [17] surface of the lake declares the everlasting immanence of God and the Son of God in the material world. *Chimborazo* (1864) is Church's ultimate in cosmic pastoral landscape. The whole cycle of a benevolent nature is contained within the picture. *The Aurora Borealis* (1865) is based upon a small and rather unprepossessing gouache of "Church's Peak" on the Coast of Labrador, painted by Dr. Isaac Hayes. Hayes, the Arctic explorer, named the landmark in honor of his artist friend. The phenomenon which the Smithsonian painting depicts was Church's addition to the composition. A display of northern lights which he and thousands of other Americans (including Herman Melville) had seen on December 23, 1864, was interpreted as a portent of Union victory. Church then straightway consulted his earlier sketches of this natural wonder to produce a polar drama. *Rainy Season in the Tropics* (1866) is a magnificent Andean Shangri-la, an Alpine Genesis. It is Church's *ne plus ultra* of Hope. *The Vale of St. Thomas, Jamaica* (1867) suggests Turnerian sublimity and beauty transformed in a realistic vision of prehistory. Before this cosmic window the would-be "New Man" at last might find himself standing on the soil of his own mythology. *Tropical Scenery* (1873) is a quiet elegy to the abiding harmony of the universe. Its serenity contrasts with the activism of Church's earlier landscapes and tells of the changing national psychology of the 'seventies. The premillennial expectancy of the 'fifties could not be prolonged indefinitely beyond the Civil War. The heroic spirit was waning. *Morning in the Tropics* (1877) reflects the pensiveness of the decade, while it is yet a great psychic landscape. Standing in front of this picture one finds himself present at the dawn of creation, or rather re-creation. The Savior, "the light of the world," appears in this beautiful primeval scene in the form of a radiant cross. Human history is forgotten as the spectator seems to awaken from nothingness to behold a strange and wonderful new world. Poetically he becomes a second Adam.

The Aegean Sea (c. 1878) is a last and not altogether successful cosmic pronouncement. Here the interest in striking effect seems to compete with the utterance of conviction. To suggest the renewal of oldness was an especially American idea. But the result appears too contrived. Church was in danger of having not enough to say. As the actual America departed further from the ideal America, Church found it harder to paint with the authority of a prophet. He had exhausted the possibilities of Old World subjects, and the New World had lost its virginity. But the roots of the crisis went still deeper. There had been a revolution in science. Within the twenty years since the publication of Darwin's *Origin of Species* (1859) the concept of a world governed by "Design" had been hopelessly undermined. Increasingly uncertain of his universe, Church could no longer paint clarion annunciations to his fellow men. *The Mediterranean Sea* (1882) is a picture of "the past in its pastness," without any sign of promise for the future. *The Iceberg* (1891) is Church's very personal response to the *fin de siècle*. It is the picture of a memory rather than of a millennium.

In the last decades of his life Church's imaginative energies were concentrated (happily for posterity's sake) on Olana, his "Center of the World." There on a hill which rises some five hundred feet above the Hudson River and surveys a panorama of the Catskills the painter created a paradise for himself. On a large estate he maintained a farm, formed a lake, built over seven miles of roads, and "laid out views." On top of his private mountain he conceived a kind of Noah's Ark of human achievement. His house, filled with a representative sampling of all that science and art could offer nineteenth-century man, was a synthesis of "Persian" and occidental styles designed to communicate with the ever-evolving life of nature which surrounded it. This extraordinary entity is in effect a domestic cathedral of the Transcendentalist [19] mystique of American destiny: the New World as the meeting of East and West, civilization and nature.

Frederic Edwin Church is surely one of our most profoundly American artists. A "Yankee of Yankees," this archetypal New Englander was born with the right talents, at the right time, at the right place. He supplied the paramount artistic need of his day, the realistic recreation and spiritual interpretation of nature. Thomas Cole, his teacher, set him on the proper road. But Church replaced the subjectivity of the romantic Cole with the objectivity of a Thoreau. Church's nature lived regardless of personal fancy. He dramatized the New World mythology. His broad- and low-horizoned landscapes corresponded with the outlook of a continental people. His earth curved. His paintings were experiences shared with each and every American. Like Whitman, he felt with *all*.

DAVID C. HUNTINGTON
Smith College
Northampton, Massachusetts

Four views of Olana (courtesy Jinny and Wendy Neefus)

LENDERS TO THE EXHIBITION

Addison Gallery of American Art, Phillips Academy, Andover, Massachusetts
Albany Institute of History and Art, Albany, New York
Allen Memorial Art Museum, Oberlin College, Oberlin, Ohio
Lyman Allyn Museum, New London, Connecticut
John Astor, New York, New York
L. L. Beans, Trenton, New Jersey
Anderson C. Bouchelle, St. Petersburg, Florida
The Brooklyn Museum, Brooklyn, New York
The Cleveland Museum of Art, Cleveland, Ohio
The Cooper Union Museum, New York, New York
The Corcoran Gallery of Art, Washington, D. C.
Henry Melville Fuller, New York, New York
The Reverend Louis C. Gillette, Birmingham, Michigan

Mrs. Iola S. Haverstick, New York, New York
The Hecksher Museum, Huntington, New York
Mrs. Alice Judson Jones, Washington, D. C.
Mrs. Frank R. McCoy, Washington, D. C.
The Metropolitan Museum of Art, New York, New York
Mr. and Mrs. J. William Middendorf, II, New York, New York
Munson-Williams-Proctor Institute, Utica, New York
Museum of Fine Arts, St. Petersburg, Florida
National Collection of Fine Arts, Smithsonian Institution, Washington, D. C.
National Gallery of Art, Washington, D. C.
New Britain Museum of American Art, New Britain, Connecticut
Olana Preservation, Incorporated, New York, New York
Frederick Osborn, New York, New York
The executors of the Estate of Mrs. Harold Ransom, New York, New York
Miss Frances Sauvalle, Galveston, Texas
The executors of the Estate of Mrs. John Slade, New York, New York
The George Walter Vincent Smith Art Museum, Springfield, Massachusetts
The Wadsworth Atheneum, Hartford, Connecticut
The Walters Art Gallery, Baltimore, Maryland
Mrs. Vanderbilt Webb, New York, New York
Nelson C. White, Waterford, Connecticut

CHRONOLOGY OF CHURCH'S LIFE AND WORK
(Asterisks indicate works included in the catalogue)

1826   May 4: born in Hartford, Conn., the only surviving of three sons of Joseph Edward and Eliza Janes Church; father was a successful insurance adjuster.

1842/3   Living in Hartford, studying with Alexander Hamilton Emmons (1816–?) for six months, and Benjamin Hutchins Coe (1799–after 1883).

1844   June: established his residence in Catskill, N. Y., studying with Thomas Cole (to 1846). Oct.: visits East Hampton, Long Island, sketching.

1845   Feb.: sketches in the vicinity of the Mountain House, Catskill. April: at Hartford. *Scene near Hartford* (coll. of Olana). Aug.: at Madison, Conn.; further sketches of the vicinity of the Mountain House, Catskill. *Twilight among the Mountains* exhibited at the National Academy of Design (no. 321) (coll. of Olana). *Hudson Scenery* exhibited at the National Academy of Design (no. 344).

1846   Sketches in the Berkshires, near Lee and Stockbridge, Mass. *Hooker and Company Journeying Through the Wilderness from Plymouth to Hartford, in 1636* exhibited at the National Academy of Design (no. 114) (exhibition catalogue gives Hartford as his address) (Wadsworth Atheneum, Hartford, Conn.; purchased in 1846, the first documented sale of a painting by Church). *Winter Evening* exhibited at the National Academy of Design (no. 145). *Moses Viewing the Promised Land* (private coll.).

1847   *Christian on the Borders of the "Valley of the Shadow of Death," Pilgrim's Progress* exhibited at the National Academy of Design (no. 84) (Hartford given as Church's address) (coll. of Olana). *Scene on the Catskill Creek, New York* exhibited at the American Art Union (no. 78). *The Charter Oak, at Hartford* exhibited at the American Art Union (no. 118) (coll. of Olana). *Storm in the Mountains* exhibited at the American Art Union (no. 120). *Kauterskill Clove, Catskill* exhibited at the American Art Union (no. 124). *Landscape* exhibited at the American Art Union (no. 254). *July Sunset* exhibited at the National Academy of Design (no. 173) (coll. John Astor, New York). Sketches in the Berkshires.

1847/8   Moves to New York City and establishes residence in the Art Union Building, 497 Broadway (to 1858).

1848   Feb.: death of Thomas Cole, in Catskill, N. Y. Visits Rochester Falls, N. Y.; possibly first trip to Niagara Falls. July: sketching in the vicinity of New Haven, Conn. Aug.–Sept.: sketching in Vermont. Late Sept.: residing in Hartford. Elected associate of the National Academy of Design. *Morning* (Albany Institute of History and Art, Albany, N. Y.). *The River of the Water of Life* exhibited at the National Academy of Design (no. 77). *View near Stockbridge* (dated 1847) exhibited at the National Academy of

Design (no. 290) (coll. of Mrs. Alfred P. Lowell, Boston). *The River of the Water of Life* exhibited at the American Art Union (no. 28). *Lake Dunmore* exhibited at the American Art Union (no. 290). *Morning* exhibited at the American Art Union (no. 348). *Rutland Falls, Vermont* exhibited at the American Art Union (no. 360).

1848/9 Accepts William James Stillman (1828–1901) as his first pupil.

1849 Sketching in Vermont. Elected to full membership in the National Academy of Design. *Lower Falls, Rochester* (coll. Mrs. Frank R. McCoy, Washington, D. C.). *A Mountain Tempest* exhibited at the National Academy of Design (no. 38) (probably the picture in the Karolik Collection, Museum of Fine Arts, Boston, under the title of *The Harp of the Winds*). *The Plague of Darkness* exhibited at the National Academy of Design (no. 82). *West Rock, New Haven* exhibited at the National Academy of Design (no. 131) (New Britain Museum of American Art, New Britain, Conn.). *Above the Clouds at Sunrise* exhibited at the American Art Union (no. 22) (coll. of L. L. Beans, Trenton, N. J.). *View in Pittsford, Vermont* exhibited at the American Art Union (no. 41). *Evening after a Storm* exhibited at the American Art Union (no. 140). *The Plague of Darkness* exhibited at the American Art Union (no. 151). *A Passing Storm* exhibited at the American Art Union (no. 358). *Morning* exhibited at the American Art Union (no. 363). *Sunset* exhibited at the American Art Union (no. 375).

1850 Joins the Century Association, New York. July–Aug.: trip through Vermont and New Hampshire (White Mountains), thence to Maine (Mount Desert Island). *Ira Mountain, Vermont* exhibited at the National Academy of Design (no. 42) (coll. of Olana). *Autumn, a Sketch* exhibited at the National Academy of Design (no. 64). *View near Clarendon, Vermont* exhibited at the National Academy of Design (no. 97). *A Wet Day* exhibited at the National Academy of Design (no. 323). *Twilight, "Short Arbiter 'Twixt Day and Night"* exhibited at the National Academy of Design (no. 349) (Newark Museum, Newark, N. J.). *On Otter Creek* exhibited at the American Art Union (no. 14). *Twilight* exhibited at the American Art Union (no. 41). *Sunset* exhibited at the American Art Union (no. 58). *View of Blackwell's Island, New York* exhibited at the American Art Union (no. 193). **Ira Mountain, Vermont* exhibited at the American Art Union (no. 216). *View near Clarendon, Vermont* exhibited at the American Art Union (no. 233). *Landscape* exhibited at the American Art Union (no. 243). *Twilight, "Short Arbiter 'Twixt Day and Night"* exhibited at the American Art Union (no. 261).

1850/1   Accepts Jervis McEntee (1828–1891) as his second pupil.

1851   June: trip through Virginia, North Carolina(?), Kentucky, and the Upper Mississippi River region with Cyrus W. Field. July: sketching in the Catskills. Aug.: trip to Grand Manan Island and the Bay of Fundy. Oct.: visits Mount Desert Island, Maine. *The Deluge* exhibited at the National Academy of Design (no. 1). *An Old Boat* exhibited at the National Academy of Design (no. 166) (Parthenon Museum, Nashville, Tenn.). *Otter Creek and Mount Desert Island, Coast of Maine* exhibited at the Pennsylvania Academy of the Fine Arts, Philadelphia (no. 37) (coll. of Arthur D. K. Healy, Middlebury, Vt.). **New England Scenery* (George Walter Vincent Smith Art Museum, Springfield, Mass.). **Beacon off Mount Desert* exhibited at the National Academy of Design (no. 371) (coll. of Mrs. Vanderbilt Webb, New York). *Lake Scene in Mount Desert* exhibited at the National Academy of Design (no. 383) (coll. of R. Henry Thorndike, Bar Harbor, Maine).

1851   *Fog off Mount Desert Island, Maine* exhibited at the American Art Union (no. 135). *The Deluge* exhibited at the American Art Union (no. 264). *Beacon off Mount Desert Island* exhibited at the American Art Union (no. 266).

1851/2 Elected an officer of the National Academy of Design.

1852   Aug.: at Grand Manan Island and Mount Katahdin, Maine. Sept.: sketching in the Catskills. *New England Scenery* exhibited at the Pennsylvania Academy of the Fine Arts, Philadelphia (no. 141), and sold by the American Art Union for $1300, the highest price paid to date for a work by Church. *The Wreck* exhibited at the National Academy of Design (no. 145). *Home by the Lake* exhibited at the National Academy of Design (no. 456) (Walker Art Center, Minneapolis, Minn.). *Natural Bridge* exhibited at the Royal Academy, London (University of Virginia, Charlottesville). *Fog off Mount Desert Island, Maine* sold, New York, American Art Union (no. 119, for $50). *The Deluge* sold, New York, American Art Union (no. 235, for $300). *Beacon off Mount Desert Island* sold, New York, American Art Union (no. 350, for $380).

1853   April–Oct.: first trip to South America, with Cyrus W. Field as his traveling companion. Late April: arrives in Barranquilla, Colombia. May 9: Barranquilla. May 10: begins trip by steamer up the Magdalena River. May 12: Mompos (thence to Nares and Conejo, and by open boat to Honda). June: Bogotá; Tequendama Falls. July 9: Fusugasuga (between Bogotá and Ibague). July 16: Ibague. July 23: Cartago (thence to Buga and Cali). Aug. 5: Popayan (one week near Purese volcano; thence to Pasto). Aug. 24: Tuquerres. Aug. 26: crosses the border into Ecuador (thence down the Chota

Valley to Ibarra). Aug.: Quito (for ten days); Pinchincha volcano. Sept. 9: Machachi (views Cotopaxi). Sept. 10–11: San Juan. Sept. 14: Riobamba (sketches Chimborazo and Tungague Mountains). Sept. 19: ascends Chimborazo. Sept. 21: Guaranda (thence to Bodegaz on the Guayas River). Sept. 24–30: Guayaquil. Oct. 1: departs on the steamer *Bogotá* for Panama. Oct. 18: sails from Aspinwall (Colón), Panama, on the steamer *Ohio*. Oct. 29: arrives in New York. *Mount Ktaadn* (sic) exhibited at the National Academy of Design (no. 81) (ex-coll. of Mrs. John Slade, Oyster Bay, N. Y.). *The Natural Bridge, Virginia* exhibited at the National Academy of Design (no. 105) (University of Virginia, Charlottesville). *Grand Manan Island, Bay of Fundy* (painted 1852) exhibited at the National Academy of Design (no. 359) (Wadsworth Atheneum, Hartford, Conn.). *Valley of the Madawasca* exhibited at the National Academy of Design (no. 424) (possibly the picture at the University of Virginia, Charlottesville). *Sunset on the Connecticut* exhibited at the Pennsylvania Academy of the Fine Arts, Philadelphia (no. 124). *Landscape* exhibited at the Pennsylvania Academy of the Fine Arts, Philadelphia (no. 200).

1854   Aug.: visits Annapolis, Nova Scotia. Sept.: at Mount Desert Island, Maine, which is to become his favorite summer haunt (to 1860). *A Country Home* exhibited at the National Academy of Design (no. 64) (coll. of Mrs. Arthur Delafield Smith, Arlington, Va.). *A New England Lake* exhibited at the National Academy of Design (no. 124). *Falls of the Tequendama near Bogotá, New Granada* (coll. of Mr. Anderson C. Bouchelle, St. Petersburg, Fla.).

1855   *Cotopaxi* (National Collection of Fine Arts, Smithsonian Institution, Washington, D. C.). *The Cordilleras: Sunrise* exhibited at the National Academy of Design (no. 49) (coll. of Mrs. Dudley Parker, Morristown, N. J.). *Tamaca Palms* exhibited at the National Academy of Design (no. 63). *Falls of the Tequendama near Bogotá, New Granada* exhibited at the National Academy of Design (no. 74). *The Andes of Ecuador* exhibited at the Boston Athenaeum. *Landscape* exhibited at the Pennsylvania Academy of the Fine Arts, Philadelphia (no. 115). *La Magdalena* exhibited at the National Academy of Design (no. 131) (Corcoran Gallery of Art, Washington, D. C.). *The Andes of Ecuador* (coll. of J. William Middendorf, II, New York).

1856   March 19–20: visits Niagara Falls, N. Y. July 7: at Niagara Falls. July–Aug. at Mount Katahdin, Maine, with Theodore Winthrop and Charles Tracy as his traveling companions (account of trip published by Winthrop, *Life in the Open Air*, 1863). Sept.–Oct. 10: visits Niagara Falls again. Summer: visits New Hampshire and Whiteface Mountain, N. Y. *A Tropical Morning* exhibited at the National Academy of Design (no. 137). *Sunset* (Munson-Williams-Proctor Art Institute, Utica, N. Y.). *South American Landscape* (coll. of Henry Melville Fuller, New York). *South American Landscape* (National Collection of Fine Arts, Smithsonian Institution, Washington, D. C.).

1857   Spring: *Niagara* first exhibited, making Church's reputation for all time (Corcoran Gallery of Art, Washington, D. C.). *The Andes of Ecuador* exhibited at the National Academy of Design (no. 23). Summer: *Niagara* exhibited in England, bringing Church to Ruskin's attention. May–Aug.: second trip to South America, with the artist Louis Remy Mignot (1831-1870) as his traveling companion. May 15: leaves Panama for Ecuador. May 23: Guayaquil, Ecuador. End of May: journeying up the Guayas River. June 3–14: Guaranda and Guanajo. June 16–17: sketches Chimborazo; Mocho, La   [31]

Tacunga, and Machachi. June 19–24: at base of Cotopaxi volcano. June 26–27: Pichincha and Cayambe volcanoes. July 3: Quito. July 7: Riobamba, via Ambato. July 9: begins journey to Sangay volcano. July 11: begins ascent of Sangay. July 13: arrives back at Riobamba. July 21: Guaranda. July 23: Jorge. July 24: Guayaquil (returns to U.S.A. by steamer via the Isthmus of Panama). Oct. 1: visits Salisbury, Conn. *Autumn* exhibited at the National Academy of Design (no. 143) (coll. of Olana). *View of the Magdalena River* exhibited at the National Academy of Design (no. 522) (coll. of Mr. Charles T. Lark, Jr., Hackensack, N. J.). *Cotopaxi* (Art Institute, Chicago).

1858   April and/or Aug.: visits Niagara Falls. July 29: at East Hampton, N. Y. *Morning in the Tropics* purchased by William T. Walters for $555 (Walters Art Gallery, Baltimore, Md.). *Cayambe Mountain, Ecuador* (New York Historical Society, New York). Moves New York studio from 497 Broadway to the Studio Building (built the year before) at nos. 21 and 15 West 10th Street (later renumbered 45-53 West 10th Street).

1859   June 17–July 23: trip along the coast of Newfoundland and Labrador; sails with the Reverend Louis Legrand Noble from Boston to Halifax; Noble describes the trip in his book *After Icebergs with a Painter* (published in 1861), illustrated with lithographs after sketches by Church; Louis Agassiz was also on the steamer from Boston to Halifax. April 27: completes *The Heart of the Andes*, purchased by William T. Blodgett for $10,000, being the highest price to date for a painting by a living American artist (Metropolitan Museum of Art, New York); exhibited in New York and then in London, summer 1859; bought by A. T. Stewart from Blodgett in 1876 for $10,000. *Twilight, a Sketch* exhibited at the National Academy of Design (no. 384) (painted in 1858) (coll. of Olana). Engaged to Isabel Mortimer Carnes, of Dayton, Ohio.

1860   Marries Isabel Carnes. Sketching in the Catskills. Sept.: visits Mount Desert Island, Maine. Nov.: moves onto the property at Hudson, N. Y., known as The Farm. *Star in the East* exhibited at the National Academy of Design (coll. of Olana). *Twilight in the Wilderness* (sold to John T. Johnston in 1866 for $4300) (Cleveland Museum of Art, Cleveland, Ohio).

1861   Completes *The Icebergs* (also known as *The North*) (now lost) (chromolithographed). *Our Banner in the Sky* exhibited at Goupil's Gallery, New York (now lost) (chromolithographed).

1862   Oct. 26: birth of his first child, Herbert Edwin. Sketching in the Catskills. *Cotopaxi* completed (coll. of John Astor, New York). *Landscape in South America* exhibited at the Pennsylvania Academy of the Fine Arts, Philadelphia (no. 74).

1863   May–Aug.: sketching in the Catskills. Oct.: visits Clarendon Springs, Vt. *The Icebergs* exhibited in London. *Under Niagara* (dated 1862) exhibited at the Boston Athenaeum (lost; chromolithographed). *Sunrise off the Maine Coast* (Wadsworth Atheneum, Hartford, Conn.). *The Meteor* exhibited at the Pennsylvania Academy of the Fine Arts (no. 123) (coll. of Mrs. Mary Barker, La Jolla, Calif.).

1864   Oct. 22: birth of second child, Emma Francis. *Chimborazo* painted for William H. Osborn, Church's major patron (coll. of Frederick Osborn, New York). *The Heart of the Andes*, *Niagara*, and *The Andes of Ecuador* exhibited at the New York Sanitary Fair.

1865   March 18: death of his son, Herbert Edwin, of diphtheria. March 26: death
        of his daughter, Emma Francis, of diphtheria. April 24–Aug.: visits Jamaica
        with the artist Horace Walcott Robbins, Jr. (1842-1904) as his traveling
        companion. Oct. 6: sketching in Vermont (Bird Mountain). *Moonrise
        and *Sunrise (memorials to his deceased children) (both coll. of Olana).
        *The Aurora Borealis painted for William T. Blodgett, based on a sketch by
        Dr. Isaac Hayes (National Collection of Fine Arts, Smithsonian Institution,
        Washington, D. C.). The Aurora Borealis, Chimborazo, and Cotopaxi (1862)
        exhibited in London, McLean's Gallery. Mount Desert (Washington Uni-
        versity, St. Louis, Mo.).

1866   June 30–July 19: at Hudson, N. Y. Oct. 22: birth of his third child, Frederic
        Joseph. *Rainy Season in the Tropics (coll. of J. William Middendorf, II,
        New York).

1867   Feb.–Sept.: at Hudson, N. Y. (purchases the wooded hill above The Farm,
        future site of his principal residence at Olana). Late autumn: leaves for Eu-
        rope (in the company of his wife, his year-old son, Frederic Joseph, and his
        mother-in-law, Mrs. Carnes). *Vale of Saint Thomas, Jamaica (Wadsworth
        Atheneum, Hartford, Conn.). Niagara awarded the second medal in the
        Paris Exposition Universelle. Niagara Falls from the American Side (ex-coll.
        of A. T. Stewart; National Gallery of Scotland, Edinburgh). Memorial to
        Cole exhibited at the Pennsylvania Academy of the Fine Arts, Philadelphia
        (no. 242). Rainy Season in the Tropics exhibited at Paris, Exposition Uni-
        verselle. Late Oct.–early Nov.: leaves New York. Arrives in France; visits
        Paris. In London before the close of the year (one week). Back to France,
        south to Marseilles (3 days), to the Near East via steamship Pelouse.

[34] 1868 South American Landscape exhibited at the National Academy of Design.

Rainy Season in the Tropics exhibited at the National Academy of Design. *Niagara* exhibited at the National Academy of Design. Jan. 4: arrives in Alexandria, Egypt. Jan. 7: Port Said, Suez; thence to Jaffa and Beirut. Jan. 14: Beirut, Lebanon. Feb. 7: arrives at Jaffa (thence to Jerusalem and Haifa). Feb. 12: leaves Jerusalem on expedition to Petra. Feb. 13: Hebron; Mount Carmel. Feb. 17: Simu-a. Feb. 20: El Yemen. Feb. 21–23: Arabah; Mount Hor. Feb. 26–27: Petra. March 2: El Yemen. March 3: Beersheba. March 5: Jaffa, via Gaza. March 7–9: Jaffa. April 2–7: Jerusalem. April 4: Bezetha; Beirut. April 28: El Musmieh; Burak; Dur Aly. April 24–May 2: Damascus. May 4: Figit; Mount Abels. May 6: Mount Lebanon. May 6–12: Baalbek. May 15: arrives in Beirut. May 25: Beirut. May 27: Lamoca; Cyprus. May 28: Cyprus; Rhodes. May 29: Rhodes; Patmos, Samos; Mityline. May 30: Smyrna. May 31: passed Mityline and Scio; Troy and Mount Ida. June 2: the Dardanelles. June 4: Constantinople, thence up the Black Sea to the Danube. June 9: Varna, on the Black Sea; by train to Roustchwek; steamer up the Danube. By June 17: in Vienna. June 26: Berchtesgaden, Bavaria. July 8: side trip to Salzburg, Austria. Aug. 1: Austria. Aug. 2: the Rhone Valley. Aug. 5: Sollins; Abtenau, Switzerland. Aug. 6: Gossau. Aug. 8: Lake Halstead, Switzerland. Aug. 20: Lake Thun. Aug. 24: Vevey; Sion (via Interlaken); Martigny. Aug. 27–Sept. 4: Bel Alp, Aletsch Glacier. Sept. 11: Mount Rosa; Ceppo Morelli; Ponte Grande, Italy. Sept.: Florence; Perugia. Oct. 1: Terni; arrives in Rome. Nov. to early April 1869: Rome (Hotel Russie, on the Pincian). Friendship with Sanford W. Gifford.

1869   Feb. 22: birth of his second child since the death of the two in 1865, Theodore Winthrop. *The Arch of Titus* begun in collaboration with Jervis McEntee and George Healy (completed in 1871) (Newark Museum, Newark,   [35]

N. J.). *Damascus* painted. Early April: Pompeii, thence to Sicily (visited Agrigento); and Greece. April 20–24: Athens, Gulf of Corinth; Cephalonia; Corfu. April 28: Foggia; Paestum; Pompeii. April 29: Velletri. May 6: Rome. May 14: Paris. June 15: London; also visits Birmingham. June 19: sails from England on ship *Russia*. June 28: lands in New York. *Scene among the Andes* exhibited at the National Academy of Design. Sept.: at Hudson, N. Y. *Damascus* exhibited in London (subsequently destroyed).

1870   April 30: birth of his fifth child, Louis Palmer (died 1943), named for the sculptor, Erastus Dow Palmer. June: sketching in the Catskills. *Afterglow* exhibited at the National Academy of Design. **Jerusalem* (ex-coll. of Mrs. Harold Ransom, Hartford, Conn.).

1870/2   Construction of his villa atop the principal hill at Olana, Hudson, N. Y.; chooses as his architect, Calvert Vaux, in preference to Richard Morris Hunt, whose earlier project was rejected.

1870/6   Sketching and painting at Hudson, in the Catskills, Vt., and Maine (summers and autumns). Acquires property on Lake Millinocket, near Mount Katahdin, Maine (about 1876 or later) and constructs a camp, which he names Rhodora. Probable trip to North Carolina.

1871   July 17: birth of his sixth and last child, Isabel Charlotte. *The Parthenon* (Metropolitan Museum of Art, New York).

1872   Summer: probably occupying the new house at Olana for the first time with his family. *Bamboo Stems—A Study from Nature* exhibited at the National Academy of Design (no. 171). *Tropical Landscape* (Delaware Art Center, Wilmington, Del.). *South American Landscape* (Princeton University Art Museum).

1873   Oct.: visits Clarendon Springs, Vt. *El Khasné, Petra (coll. of Olana). *Syria by the Sea* (Detroit Institute of Arts, Detroit, Mich.). *Tropical Scenery* (Brooklyn Museum, Brooklyn, N. Y.).

1874   Summer: trip through the Green Mountains, Vt., with Walter Palmer (son of Erastus Dow Palmer). *El Khasné, Petra* exhibited at the National Academy of Design (no. 320). *The Three Columns* painted for William H. Osborn (coll. of Frederick Osborn, New York). *A Tropical Moonlight* painted for William H. Osborn (coll. of Frederick Osborn, New York).

1875   *Valley of the Santa Ysabel* (Berkshire Museum, Pittsfield, Mass.). *Autumn* (coll. of Mrs. Vanderbilt Webb, New York). Late winter: visits Niagara Falls for the last time (letter of March 22). *After the Rainstorm* exhibited at Goupil's Gallery, New York (now lost). Spring: *El Khasné, Petra* exhibited at Chicago, Chicago Academy of Design.

1876   Sept. 7: at Mount Katahdin, Maine. *The Parthenon* exhibited at the Philadelphia Centennial Exposition. *El Ayn* (The Fountain) (now lost). *Chimborazo* exhibited at the Philadelphia Centennial Exposition (won bronze medal). *Niagara* bought by W. W. Corcoran for $12,500.

1876 or '77   Contracts illness diagnosed as "inflammatory rheumatism" which somewhat curtails his painting activity from now on.

1877   Sept.: at Mount Katahdin, Maine. *Morning in the Tropics* (National Gallery of Art, Washington, D. C.). *The Aegean Sea* (Metropolitan Museum of Art, New York).

1878   Sept.–Oct. 2: at Mount Katahdin, Maine. *Morning in the Tropics* exhibited at Paris, Exposition Universelle. *The Parthenon* exhibited at Paris, Exposi- [37]

tion Universelle. *The Aegean Sea* exhibited at Goupil's Gallery, New York. *Evening on the Sea* exhibited at the National Academy of Design (no. 473).

1879   Oct. 1: at Mount Katahdin, Maine. *Morning in the Tropics* exhibited at the Century Association, New York. *The Monastery of Our Lady of the Snows* (Cleveland Museum of Art, Cleveland, Ohio).

1880   July: sketching at Lake George, N. Y. Fall: sketching at Lake Millinocket; later in North Carolina.

1880/1   *New England Landscape* and *Damascus* exhibited in a loan exhibition at the Metropolitan Museum of Art, New York (Oct.–Mar.).

1880–1900   Only sporadic activity in painting and sketching; winters spent in Mexico; summers divided between Olana and Lake Millinocket, Maine.

1882   June: at Hudson, N. Y. *The Mediterranean Sea* (coll. of Mrs. Iola S. Haverstick, New York).

1883   Dec.: in Mexico.

1884   Dec. 21: in Mexico.

1885   May 1: still in Mexico.

1886   Touches up *Niagara* (Corcoran Gallery of Art).

1888/9   Adds studio wing to house at Olana (ornamental woodwork by Lockwood deForest).

1889   Feb. 23–April 27: in Mexico. *Constantinople* (Kennedy Galleries, New York).

1890   Jan. 23–April 15: in Mexico.

1891   *The Iceberg* (coll. of Miss Frances Sauvalle, Galveston, Texas). *Jungle Interior* (coll. of Olana). Studio wing at Olana completed.

1893   Jan. 21–Feb. 27: in Mexico. *The Aegean Sea* exhibited at the American Fine Arts Society, London.

1895   *Mount Katahdin from Millinocket Camp*, his last dated canvas (coll. of Volkirk Whitbeck, Forest Hills, N. Y.).

1899   May 12: death of his wife.

1889–1900   Winter: in Mexico with his son Louis.

1900   March: returns to New York in feeble health. April 7: dies, a few weeks before his 74th birthday, in the home of his friend and patron, William H. Osborn, on Park Ave., New York. Buried at the side of his wife in Spring Grove Cemetery, Hartford, Conn. May 28–Oct. 15: memorial exhibition held at the Metropolitan Museum of Art.

CATALOGUE

Church's habit of reconstructing a particular setting many years after he had visited and sketched the locale being represented makes a chronological listing of his works almost impossible. A topical listing has been substituted, arranged as follows: North America, The Tropics, The Far North, The Old World, Imaginary Subjects.

In the measurements, height precedes width. Those titles in quotes are the titles originally provided by Church at the time of the first public exhibition of the work in question.

NORTH AMERICA

1. SKETCH OF A CONNECTICUT LANDSCAPE

Pencil on white paper, 10⅛ x 15¼ in.
Dated October 1844
Lent by the Cooper Union Museum, New York

During the month of October 1844 Church also visited East Hampton, Long Island.

2. SCENE NEAR HARTFORD

Oil on panel, 13¼ x 17⅛ in.
Unsigned (about 1845)
Collection: Olana
Lent by Olana Preservation, Inc.

3. AUTUMN IN THE CATSKILLS

Oil on canvas, 21 x 30 in.
Unsigned (about 1845)
Lent by the Hecksher Museum, Huntington, N. Y.

4. "MORNING"

Oil on canvas, 18 x 24 in.
Signed and dated 1848

Collection: Mrs. Catherine Ganesvoort Lansing, Albany, N. Y.; given by her to the Albany Institute of History and Art, about 1910

Exhibited: New York, the American Art Union, 1848 (no. 348)

Lent by the Albany Institute of History and Art, Albany, N. Y. (Albany showing only)

5. STUDY OF THE LOWER FALLS OF THE GENESEE RIVER, ROCHESTER, NEW YORK

Pencil and white gouache on dark olive-green paper, 12⅛ x 18⅛ in.
Dated 1848
Lent by the Cooper Union Museum, New York

This and the following drawing are studies for the painting "Lower Falls, Rochester."

6. STUDY OF THE LOWER FALLS OF THE GENESEE RIVER, ROCHESTER, NEW YORK

Pencil, 10½ x 13 in.
Dated 1848
Collection: Olana
Lent by Olana Preservation, Inc.

7. "LOWER FALLS, ROCHESTER"

Oil on canvas, 20⅛ x 30¼ in.
Signed and dated 1849

Collection: Cyrus W. Field; Isabella Field (Mrs. William Francis) Judson (his daughter); Cyrus Field Judson (her son); Mrs. Frank R. McCoy (his daughter)

Lent by Mrs. Frank R. McCoy, Washington, D. C.

8. "WEST ROCK, NEW HAVEN"

Oil on canvas, 26½ x 40 in.
Signed and dated 1849

Collection: Cyrus W. Field; Robert G. Vose Galleries, Boston; purchased by the Museum from the Vose Galleries, 1950

Exhibited: New York, National Academy of Design, 1849 (no. 131); New York, American Academy of Arts and Letters, "American Landscape," Dec. 3–30, 1954 (no. 124)

Lent by the New Britain Museum of American Art, New Britain, Conn.

9. "ABOVE THE CLOUDS AT SUNRISE"

Oil on canvas, 27¼ x 40¼ in.
Signed and dated 1849

Collection: Sold (New York, American Art Union, 1849) to R. Cranford, Jr., Brooklyn, N. Y.; George Whitney, New York (sold, New York, American Art Galleries, Dec. 16–18, 1885, no. 73, for $500); W. P. A. Waggeman; Professor Sloane, Princeton, N. J. (sold, 1954)

Exhibited: New York, American Art Union, 1849 (no. 22)

Lent by Mr. L. L. Beans, Trenton, N. J.

10. "IRA MOUNTAIN, VERMONT"

Oil on canvas, 40 x 60 in.
Unsigned (dated about 1849–50)

Collection: sold to Azel B. Hull, Angelica, N. Y.; bought back by the artist (after 1850); Olana

Exhibited: New York, National Academy of Design,

1850 (no. 42); New York, American Art Union, 1850 (no. 216)

Lent by Olana Preservation, Inc.

11. WOODLAND SCENE

Pencil and oil on cardboard, 9¼ x 11¾ in.
Undated (about 1850)
Lent by the Cooper Union Museum, New York

The locale could be Mount Desert Island, Maine

12. A SNAPPED TREE TRUNK

Pencil and white gouache on grey paper, 11¾ x 15 in.
Undated (about 1850)
Collection: Olana
Lent by Olana Preservation, Inc.

13. STUDY OF MOUNT DESERT ISLAND, MAINE

Pencil and white gouache on grey paper, 9¼ x 15 in.
Undated (about 1850)
Collection: Olana
Lent by Olana Preservation, Inc.

14. STUDY FOR "NEW ENGLAND SCENERY"

Oil on panel, 12 x 15 in.
Signed and dated 1850

Collection: purchased from the artist by William Dusenbery Sherrerd, Philadelphia; James Hunt Sherrerd (his son); Ellen Sherrerd (Mrs. Sidney) Mason (his daughter); Miss Evelyn Page Mason (her niece), who presented it to the Museum

Lent by the Lyman Allyn Museum, New London, Conn.

This work is a study for the painting in the Smith Art Museum, Springfield, Mass.

15. "NEW ENGLAND SCENERY"

Oil on canvas, 33¾ x 53 in.
Signed and dated 1851

Collection: purchased from the artist by the American Art Union for $500 (sold, New York, American Art Union sale, Dec. 16–18, 1852, for $1300, being the highest price to date for a painting by Church); G. Daniels; Robert M. Olyphant (sold, New York, Somerville Gallery, Dec. 18–19, 1877, for $1425); David Dow; purchased by the Museum from Dow's widow in 1916

Exhibited: New York, American Art Union, 1851 (no. 354); Chicago, Art Institute of Chicago, and New York, Whitney Museum of American Art, "The Hudson River School," Feb.–May 1945 (no. 40, reprod.); New York, Wildenstein and Co., "A Loan Exhibition of Great American Paintings—Landmarks in American Art, 1670 1950," Feb. 26 March 28, 1953 (no. 20); Northampton, Smith College Museum of Art, "Master and Pupil: Thomas Cole and Frederick Church," Nov. 1–Dec. 4, 1958 (no. 12)

Lent by the George Walter Vincent Smith Art Museum, Springfield, Mass.

16. SKETCH OF A HILLSIDE, NORTH CAROLINA

Pencil and white gouache on grey paper, 10⅝ x 7⅛ in.
Undated (probably June 1851)
Lent by the Cooper Union Museum, New York

17. SKETCH OF A TREETOP

Pencil, 11⅜ x 9⅛ in.
Dated 1851
Collection: Olana
Lent by Olana Preservation, Inc.

This detail is found in the painting "Sunset," completed five years later.

18. SUNSET ON THE MAINE COAST

Pencil and oil on paper, 9 x 14 in.
Undated (probably 1850–55)
Lent by the Cooper Union Museum, New York

The setting is probably Mount Desert Island.

19. LUMBER MILL, MOUNT DESERT ISLAND

Pencil and white gouache on cream-colored paper, 10¼ x 15 in.
Undated (probably 1850–51)
Collection: Olana
Lent by Olana Preservation, Inc.

20. GROUP OF TREES, MOUNT DESERT ISLAND

Pencil and white gouache on grey paper, 11¼ x 14½ in.
Undated (about 1850)

15. *New England Scenery*

Collection: Olana
Lent by Olana Preservation, Inc.

21. ROCKS OFF GRAND MANAN ISLAND, CANADA

Oil on cardboard, $9\frac{7}{8}$ x $16\frac{1}{16}$ in.
Undated (September 1851)
Lent by the Cooper Union Museum, New York

A related drawing (Cooper Union Museum) identifies the scene and is dated Sept. 2, 1851.

22. "BEACON OFF MOUNT DESERT"

Oil on canvas, 31 x 46 in.
Signed and dated 1851

Collection: sold, New York, American Art Union, 1852 (no. 350) for $380; H. W. Aspinwall; William Henry Osborn, New York (?); William Church Osborn (his son); Aileen Osborn (Mrs. Vanderbilt) Webb (his daughter)

Exhibited: New York, National Academy of Design, 1851 (no. 371); New York, American Art Union, 1851 (no. 266)

Lent by Mrs. Vanderbilt Webb, New York

23. "KTAADN FROM KTAADN LAKE"

Pencil, 12 x $17\frac{3}{4}$ in.
Dated September 3, 1852
Collection: Olana
Lent by Olana Preservation, Inc.

This is a study for the painting "Mount Ktaadn" of the following year.

24. "MOUNT KTAADN"

Oil on canvas, 36 x 55 in.
Signed and dated 1853

Collection: Marshall O. Roberts, New York (sold, New York, American Art Association, January 19, 1897); Townsend Underhill, New York; Mrs. John Slade, Oyster Bay, New York (his granddaughter)

Exhibited: New York, National Academy of Design, 1853 (no. 81)

Lent by the executors of the Estate of Mrs. John Slade, New York

25. STUDY FOR "SUNSET"

Oil on cardboard (mounted on canvas), $9\frac{3}{4}$ x $17\frac{1}{4}$ in. (cardboard)
Unsigned (about 1855)
Collection: Olana
Lent by Olana Preservation, Inc.

26. "SUNSET"

Oil on canvas, 24 x 36 in.
Signed and dated 1856

Collection: Utica Art Association; Mrs. James Watson Williams, Utica (1879); Frederick T. Proctor (her son-in-law) (listed in the inventory of his estate, 1888)

Exhibited: Chicago, Art Institute of Chicago, and New York, Whitney Museum of American Art, "The Hudson River School," Feb.–May 1945 (no.

24. *Mount Ktaadn*

42, reprod.); New York, American Academy of Arts and Letters, "The Great Decade in American Writing, with Paintings by Friends and Contemporaries of the Authors," Dec. 3–30, 1954; Waterville, Maine, Colby College, Boston, Museum of Fine Arts, and New York, Whitney Museum of American Art, "Maine and Its Artists, 1710–1963," May–Aug. 1963 (no. 25, reprod.)

Lent by the Munson-Williams-Proctor Institute, Utica, N. Y.

27. "SUNSET"

Oil on canvas, 16¼ x 24¼ in.
Unsigned (1856)

Collection: painted for Church's friend, the sculptor Erastus Dow Palmer, Albany, N. Y. (in January 1856, according to an inscription on the back of the canvas); Miss Beatrice Palmer (his granddaughter); given by her to the Albany Institute of History and Art, 1942

Lent by the Albany Institute of History and Art, Albany, N. Y. (Albany showing only)

This work may constitute a recollection on the part of the artist of his painting of 1850, "Twilight, 'Short Arbiter 'Twixt Day and Night' " (not included in the present exhibition).

28. VIEW OF MOUNT DESERT, MAINE

Pencil and oil on cardboard, 11⅜ x 17 9/16 in.
Undated (1855–60)
Lent by the Cooper Union Museum, New York

29. MOUNT KATAHDIN

Oil on canvas, 8 x 11¾ in.
Unsigned (1856)

Collection: given by the artist to his friend Theodore Winthrop; Winslow Ames, Saunderstown, R. I.; given to the Addison Gallery of American Art by Mr. Ames in memory of Edward Winslow Ames

Lent by the Addison Gallery of American Art, Phillips Academy, Andover, Mass.

In 1856 Church, with his friends Theodore Winthrop and Charles Tracy, penetrated the Maine woods into the area now known as Acadia National Park, and ascended Katahdin. Church's party then canoed down the Penobscot West Branch. Winthrop vividly describes the trip in his book *Life in the Open Air*, published in 1863.

30. NIAGARA FALLS FROM GOAT ISLAND IN WINTER

Oil on cardboard, 11½ x 17⅜ in.
Dated March 1856
Lent by the Cooper Union Museum, New York

Terrapin Tower, off Goat Island on the American side of the Falls, was demolished in 1873 as being too hazardous for further use by the public.

31. STUDY OF NIAGARA FALLS FROM THE AMERICAN SIDE, WINTER

Pencil and white gouache (oxidized) on grey paper, 12 x 17 9/16 in.

31. Study of Niagara Falls from the American Side, Winter

Dated March 21, 1856
Lent by the Cooper Union Museum, New York

32. BASE OF NIAGARA FALLS

Oil on cardboard, 11⅝ x 13¾ in.
Undated (possibly July 1856)
Lent by the Cooper Union Museum, New York

33. GORGE OF THE NIAGARA RIVER

Oil on cardboard, 10¾ x 16$\frac{7}{16}$ in.
Undated (probably September 1856)
Lent by the Cooper Union Museum, New York

34. STUDY OF NIAGARA FALLS

Pencil and white gouache (oxidized) on light brown
paper, 11⅛ x 18 in.
Dated October 1856
Lent by the Cooper Union Museum, New York

35. STUDY OF NIAGARA FALLS FROM THE CANADIAN SIDE

Pencil and white gouache (oxidized) on dark brown
paper, 10$\frac{13}{16}$ x 12$\frac{5}{16}$ in.
Dated October 1856
Lent by the Cooper Union Museum, New York

36. SIX SKETCHES OF NIAGARA FALLS

Pencil and white gouache on grey-brown paper, 3½
x 6⅛ in. (average size)
Dated 1856
Lent by the Cooper Union Museum, New York

37. NIAGARA FALLS

Oil on canvas, 12 x 35 in.
Unsigned (about 1856)

Collection: given by the artist to his daughter, Isabel
Charlotte (Mrs. Jeremiah Sullivan) Gillette; Louis
Black Gillette (her son); Louis Church Gillette (his
son)

Lent by the Reverend Louis C. Gillette, Birmingham,
Mich.

38. NIAGARA FALLS

Oil on canvas, 12 x 36 in.
Unsigned (about 1856–57)
Collection: Olana
Lent by Olana Preservation, Inc.

39. "NIAGARA"

Oil on canvas, 42¼ x 90½ in.
Signed and dated 1857

Collection: sold by the artist to Williams and Stevens
(trade), New York (for $2500 plus $2000 for chromolithograph rights); anonymous owner; John Taylor Johnston, New York (who bought it from a bank
for $5000 before 1867) (sold, New York, Chicker-
ing Hall, Dec. 1876, for $12,500); purchased at the
Johnston sale by William Wilson Corcoran, Washington, D. C.

Exhibited: New York, Williams and Stevens, April
1857; London, summer 1857; Boston, Williams and
Everett's Gallery, Dec. 1859–Feb. 1860; New York,

41. Study of a Forest Pool (photo courtesy of the Frick Art Reference Library)

Metropolitan Fair (Sanitary Commission), April 1864; Paris, Exposition Universelle, 1867 (won second class medal); New York, National Academy of Design, 1868; New York, Metropolitan Museum of Art and National Academy of Design, "Centennial Loan Exhibition," 1876 (no. 190); New York, Metropolitan Museum of Art, "Paintings by Frederic E. Church, N.A.," May 28–Oct. 15, 1900 (reprod.); San Francisco, Panama-Pacific International Exposition, 1915; Pittsburgh, Carnegie Institute, Dept. of Fine Arts, "Survey of American Painting," Oct. 24–Dec. 15, 1940 (no. 97, reprod.); Washington, Corcoran Gallery of Art, "De Gustibus—An Exhibition of American Painting Illustrating a Century of Taste and Criticism," Jan. 9–Feb. 20, 1949 (no. 12, reprod.); Wilmington, University of Delaware and Wilmington Society of Fine Arts, Delaware Art Center, "American Painting 1857–1869," Jan. 10–Feb. 18, 1962 (no. 13, reprod.); Buffalo, Albright-Knox Art Gallery, "Three Centuries of Niagara Falls," May 2–Sept. 7, 1964 (no. 23, reprod.)

Lent by the Corcoran Gallery of Art, Washington, D. C. (Washington showing only)

Unquestionably Church's most popular and famous work today, "Niagara" has suffered many vicissitudes and much criticism. At the time the picture was in Johnston's possession it began to show signs of streaking, which Church explained was caused by the use of "sugar of lead in the preparation of the canvas—to promote haste in drying." The sky was repainted at that time. Then in 1886 the bursting of a steam pipe in the old Corcoran Gallery so damaged the painting that it was sent to Olana in order that Church might repaint the sky for a second time. He admitted that if there had been "no engravings of the picture" he would have permitted himself "more freedom." On a later visit to Washington, in 1890, he "was surprised to see that the sky was still 'dead.' "

Universally acclaimed as "brilliant" and "superior" and having drawn tremendous crowds everywhere it was exhibited, always by itself, it was also boldly attacked as containing a surfeit of "nauseous detail" by at least one critic, while another helpfully pointed out that the best way to view the painting was through a tube. In any case, it represents one of the greatest tours de force of topographical painting ever attempted.

40. "TWILIGHT, A SKETCH"

Oil on canvas, 8 x 12 in.
Signed and dated 1858
Collection: Olana
Exhibited: New York, National Academy of Design, 1859 (no. 384)
Lent by Olana Preservation, Inc.

41. STUDY OF A FOREST POOL

Oil on canvas, 12½ x 12½ in.
Undated (about 1860)
Collection: Olana
Lent by Olana Preservation, Inc.

The locale is probably Maine.

42. MOUNTS KATAHDIN AND TURNER FROM KATAHDIN
    LAKE, MAINE

Pencil and oil on cardboard, $12\frac{1}{16}$ x 20 in.
Undated (1856 or before)
Lent by the Cooper Union Museum, New York

43. LANDSCAPE SKETCH WITH A RAINBOW

Pencil and white chalk on olive-green paper, $4\frac{3}{8}$ x
$7\frac{1}{4}$ in.
Lent by the Cooper Union Museum, New York

A leaf from a sketchbook dated 1860.

44. "TWILIGHT IN THE WILDERNESS"

Oil on canvas, 40 x 64 in.
Signed and dated 1860

Collection: John Taylor Johnston, New York (sold,
New York, Chickering Hall, Dec. 1876, for $3600);
Miss M. E. Garrett, Baltimore (1900); Robert W.
DeForest; Talbot DeForest (his son); Robert Wei-
mann, Ansonia, Conn. (1965)

Exhibited: New York, Goupil's Gallery, June 1860;
Paris, Exposition Universelle, 1867; New York, Met-
ropolitan Museum of Art and National Academy of
Design, "Centennial Loan Exhibition," 1876 (no.
242); New York, Metropolitan Museum of Art,
"Paintings by Frederic E. Church, N.A.," May 28–
Oct. 15, 1900 (reprod.)

Lent by the Cleveland Museum of Art, Cleveland,
Ohio (Mr. and Mrs. William H. Marlatt Fund)

45. VIEW FROM BIRD MOUNTAIN, VERMONT

Pencil on greenish paper, $10\frac{1}{2}$ x $16\frac{1}{16}$ in.
Dated October 1863
Lent by the Cooper Union Museum, New York

The scene is in the neighborhood of Clarendon
Springs, Vt., a favored haunt of many years' standing with the artist.

46. "SUNRISE OFF THE MAINE COAST" (also known as
    "STORM AT MOUNT DESERT")

Oil on canvas, 37 x 47 in.
Signed and dated 1863

Collection: Marshall O. Roberts, New York; Mrs.
Clara Hinton Gould; bequeathed by Mrs. Gould to
the museum, 1948

Exhibited: Hartford, Wadsworth Atheneum, "Gould
Bequest of American Art," Sept. 10–Oct. 3, 1948;
ibid., "A Second Look: Late 19th-Century Taste in
Painting," July 8–Aug. 6, 1958 (no. 8)

Lent by the Wadsworth Atheneum, Hartford, Conn.

47. STUDY OF BIRCH TREES

Oil on cardboard, 12 x $7\frac{11}{16}$ in.
Dated October 1865
Lent by the Cooper Union Museum, New York

This study may have been made on Church's trip to
Vermont in the autumn of 1865.

48. AUTUMN LANDSCAPE NEAR CASTLETON, VERMONT

Oil on canvas, 12 x 20 in.

Signed (about 1865)
Collection: Olana
Lent by Olana Preservation, Inc.

49. WOODLAND SCENE

Pencil and oil on cardboard, 9⅛ x 12¹⁵⁄₁₆ in.
Undated (about 1865–75)
Lent by the Cooper Union Museum, New York

50. Two sketches: CLOUD STUDIES; VIEW OF THE HUDSON AT WEST POINT, LOOKING NORTH

Pencil on cream-colored paper, 4⅝ x 8⁹⁄₁₆ in. (each)
Lent by the Cooper Union Museum, New York

These sheets come from a sketchbook dating from June–July 1866. The Hudson River landscape relates to a painting in the collection of Mrs. A. Perry Osborn, Garrison, N. Y.

51. GOLDFISH IN A POND

Oil on cardboard, 12¼ x 14½ in.
Undated (probably 1870–80)
Collection: Olana
Lent by Olana Preservation, Inc.

This work illustrates the type of unusual subject matter which Church treated occasionally.

52. WINTER SCENE, OLANA

Oil on canvas, 11 x 17½ in.
Undated (probably the early 1870's)
Collection: Olana

Lent by Olana Preservation, Inc.

This view looking southwest is taken from below the terrace of his house, which Church designed to be recessed into the building proper so that he could paint in comfort in all weather.

53. AUTUMN

Oil on canvas, 15 x 24 in.
Signed and dated 1875

Collection: William Henry Osborn (?); William Church Osborn (his son); Aileen Osborn (Mrs. Vanderbilt) Webb (his daughter)

Lent by Mrs. Vanderbilt Webb, New York

54. HILLS NEAR OLANA IN WINTER SUNSET

Oil on cardboard, 6⅞ x 12⅛ in.
Undated (about 1875–90)
Lent by the Cooper Union Museum, New York

55. VIEW OF OLANA FROM THE SOUTHWEST

Pencil and oil on cardboard, 12⅛ x 9½ in.
Undated (about 1875–80)
Lent by the Cooper Union Museum, New York

This view shows Church's house before the addition of the studio wing, carried out between 1888 and 1891.

56. VIEW LOOKING SOUTHWEST FROM OLANA

Oil on cardboard, 7¼ x 11¹⁄₁₆ in.

55. View of Olana from the Southwest

Dated 1882
Lent by the Cooper Union Museum, New York

57. MAINE CAMPFIRE

Oil on canvas, 12 x 20¼ in.
Collection: Olana
Lent by Olana Preservation, Inc.

This composition was the subject of an illustration in an article by A. L. Holley, "Camps and Tramps about Ktaadn" (*Scribner's Monthly*, May 1878, pp. 33–40). The trip was made in September 1877, and the party included Church, Sanford Gifford, H. W. Robbins, and Lockwood deForest, all artists, and the author of the article as well.

THE TROPICS

58. TWO HOUSES IN BARRANQUILLA, COLOMBIA

Pencil and oil on paper, $12\frac{7}{16}$ x $17\frac{9}{16}$ in.
Dated April 1853
Lent by the Cooper Union Museum, New York

59. PORTRAIT OF JUSTINIANO DE LA ROSA, BARRAN-
      QUILLA, COLOMBIA

Oil on cardboard, 8¾ x 8½ in.
Dated May 1853
Lent by the Cooper Union Museum, New York

60. SKETCHES FROM BOGOTÁ, COLOMBIA

Pencil and opaque watercolors on olive-green paper,

$10\frac{13}{16}$ x 14⅝ in.
Undated (June 1853)
Lent by the Cooper Union Museum, New York

This sketch constitutes Church's only known work in the realm of watercolor, save the studies he made of polychromed brick and tilework in the designs for Olana.

61. FIRST STUDY FOR "FALLS OF THE TEQUENDAMA NEAR
      BOGOTÁ, NEW GRANADA"

Pencil and white gouache (oxidized) on brown paper, $17\frac{9}{16}$ x 12 in.
Undated (June 1853)
Lent by the Cooper Union Museum, New York

At least six other views of these falls and their setting were recorded by Church's pencil.

62. SECOND STUDY FOR "FALLS OF THE TEQUENDAMA
      NEAR BOGOTÁ, NEW GRANADA"

Pencil and white gouache (oxidized) on brown paper, $17\frac{1}{16}$ x 10¼ in.
Undated (June 1853)
Lent by the Cooper Union Museum, New York

For the final painting the artist chose this view in preference to that seen in the previous drawing.

63. "FALLS OF THE TEQUENDAMA NEAR BOGOTÁ, NEW
      GRANADA"

Oil on canvas, 64 x 40 in.
Signed and dated 1854

[57]

Collection: painted for Cyrus W. Field; Isabella Field (Mrs. William Francis) Judson (his daughter); Cyrus Field Judson (her son); Mr. R. Wesley Smith, Sebring, Fla. (1965)

Exhibited: New York, National Academy of Design, 1855 (no. 74); New York, Metropolitan Museum of Art, "Paintings by Frederic E. Church, N.A.," May 28–Oct. 15, 1900 (reprod.)

Lent by Mr. Anderson C. Bouchelle through the Museum of Fine Arts, St. Petersburg, Fla.

New Granada was the name by which Colombia was formerly known.

64. THREE SOUTH AMERICAN SKETCHES: The Peak of Cayambe, Ecuador; Church at Tuquerres, Colombia; Cathedral at Popayan, Colombia

Pencil on cream-colored paper, 4⅞ x 7⅞ in. (each)
Dated August 5 and 29, 1853
Lent by the Cooper Union Museum, New York

These studies come from the same dismembered sketchbook.

65. DISTANT VIEW OF COTOPAXI, ECUADOR

Pencil on cream-colored paper, 10¾ x 17⅞ in.
Undated (September 1853)
Lent by the Cooper Union Museum, New York

66. "COTOPAXI"

Oil on canvas, 28⅛ x 42⅛ in.

Signed and dated 1855

Collection: painted for Cyrus W. Field, Isabella Field (Mrs. William Francis) Judson (his daughter); Cyrus Field Judson (her son); Mrs. Frank R. McCoy (his daughter); given to the National Collection of Fine Arts by Mrs. McCoy (1965)

Exhibited: New York, Metropolitan Museum of Art, "Paintings by Frederic E. Church, N.A.," May 28–Oct. 15, 1900 (reprod.)

Lent by the National Collection of Fine Arts, Smithsonian Institution, Washington, D. C.

67. "THE ANDES OF ECUADOR"

Oil on canvas, 48 x 75 in.
Signed and dated 1855

Collection: painted for William Henry Osborn; Mrs. William H. Osborn; A. Perry Osborn (their son); Mrs. A. Perry Osborn (sold 1965)

Exhibited: Boston, Boston Athenaeum, "Twenty-Eighth Exhibition of Paintings and Statuary at the Athenaeum Gallery," 1855; New York, National Academy of Design, 1857 (no. 23); New York, Metropolitan Fair Sanitary Commission, April 1864; New York, Metropolitan Museum of Art, "Paintings by Frederic E. Church, N.A.," May 28–Oct. 15, 1900 (reprod.)

Lent by Mr. and Mrs. J. William Middendorf, II, New York

68. SOUTH AMERICAN LANDSCAPE

Oil on canvas, 23⅜ x 35½ in.

62. Second Study of the Falls of the Tequendama

63. *The Falls of the Tequendama*

66. *Cotopaxi*

Signed and dated 1856

Collection: Mrs. Theresa Davis McCagg, Washington, D. C. (1917)

Lent by the National Collection of Fine Arts, Smithsonian Institution, Washington, D. C.

It is possible that this is the picture exhibited at the National Academy of Design in 1856 under the title of *A Tropical Morning* (no. 137) as having been lent by G. T. Olyphant. A somewhat similar undated painting, of almost the same dimensions, is in the Virginia Museum of Fine Arts, Richmond.

69. SOUTH AMERICAN LANDSCAPE

Oil on canvas, $14\frac{1}{2}$ x $21\frac{1}{2}$ in.
Signed and dated 1856

Collection: painted for John Earl Williams (as a companion piece to an autumn landscape entitled "North America," now lost); the Misses Williams (his daughters); Miss Fanny Mustin (their servant, who inherited the picture from them); Leroy Ireland (about 1957); French and Company, New York; Dr. Mark Sheppard, Tampa, Fla.

Lent by Mr. Henry Melville Fuller, New York

70. HOUSETOPS, ECUADOR

Oil on cardboard, $13\frac{7}{8}$ x $11\frac{7}{16}$ in.
Dated May 1857
Lent by the Cooper Union Museum, New York

The setting is probably Guyaquil, where Church landed in late May of that year.

71. PANORAMIC VIEW OF GUARANDA, ECUADOR

Pencil and white gouache on greenish-grey paper, $12\frac{1}{4}$ x $17\frac{1}{4}$ in.
Dated June 8, 1857
Lent by the Cooper Union Museum, New York

72. VIEW OF CHIMBORAZO, ECUADOR

Pencil and oil on Academy board, $13\frac{5}{8}$ x $20\frac{15}{16}$ in.
Undated (probably June 16–17, 1857)
Lent by the Cooper Union Museum, New York

73. STUDIES OF CAYAMBE AND SINCHOLAGUA, ECUADOR

Pencil and white gouache on grey paper, 7 x 10 in.
Dated June 24, 1857
Lent by the Cooper Union Museum, New York

74. THE ANDES OF ECUADOR FROM THE HACIENDA CHILLO

Pencil and white gouache on grey paper, 14 x $21\frac{5}{8}$ in.
Dated June 27, 1857
Lent by the Cooper Union Museum, New York

The Hacienda Chillo is probably Chillogallo of to-day, in the vicinity of Quito. This panorama of the Cordilleras includes Cotachachi, Cayambe, Antisana, Cotopaxi, Corazon, Iliniza, and Pichincha, all peaks well known to the readers of Humboldt's *Cosmos*.

75. SANGAY VOLCANO, ECUADOR, ERUPTING

Pencil and oil on cardboard, $8\frac{15}{16}$ x $14\frac{5}{16}$ in.

Undated (probably July 9–11, 1857)
Lent by the Cooper Union Museum, New York

76. CHIMBORAZO FROM RIOBAMBA, ECUADOR

Pencil and white gouache on cream-colored paper, 13⅞ x 21¾ in.
Dated July 14, 1857
Lent by the Cooper Union Museum, New York

Church was staying at the house of Pablo Bustamente, Governor of Riobamba, from where the party made the journey to Sangay volcano.

77. SOUTH AMERICAN RIVER SCENE

Oil on cardboard, 6¼ x 11½ in.
Undated (1857)
Collection: Olana
Lent by Olana Preservation, Inc.

78. "MORNING IN THE TROPICS"

Oil on canvas, 8¼ x 14 in.
Unsigned (about 1858)

Collection: donated by the artist to the National Academy of Design (sold for the benefit of the William Ranney Fund, Dec. 20, 1858, for $555); William Thompson Walters (bought at the Ranney Fund sale)

Exhibited: New York, The Century Association, Feb. 1858; Baltimore, Baltimore Museum of Art, "A Souvenir of Romanticism in America," May 10–June 10, 1940; U. S. Department of State, "60 Americans Since 1800," New York, Grand Central Galleries, Nov. 19–Dec. 5, 1946 and Cairo International Exhibition, Jan. 1947; American Federation of Arts traveling exhibition, "Major Work in Minor Scale," 1959–60

Lent by the Walters Art Gallery, Baltimore, Md.

The Boston *Daily Evening Transcript* (Jan. 21, 1861) stated that the price this picture fetched at the Ranney Fund sale was "the highest ever given in this country for so small a landscape." Engraved in steel about 1860.

79. STUDY FOR "THE HEART OF THE ANDES"

Oil on canvas, 10 x 18 in.
Signed and dated 1858
Collection: Olana
Lent by Olana Preservation, Inc.

80. "THE HEART OF THE ANDES"

Steel engraving, 13½ x 24⅞ in. (picture area)
Collection: Olana
Lent by Olana Preservation, Inc.

Engraved by William Forrest, in Edinburgh. Published in London, 1863 (after "three years' labor of ten hours a day," according to *Harper's Weekly*, vol. 7, April 4, 1863, p. 210). Proofs signed by the artist sold for $30 apiece. The engraving is after the picture, considered in Church's own day his most important work, today in the Metropolitan Museum of Art. Due to the precarious condition of the paint sur-

82. *Cotopaxi*

face, the picture is not available for the present exhibition.

81. STUDY FOR "COTOPAXI"

Oil on canvas, 9 x 13½ in.
Signed and dated 1861
Lent by Mr. Nelson C. White, Waterford, Conn.

82. "COTOPAXI"

Oil on canvas, 50 x 100 in.
Signed and dated 1862
Collection: purchased from the artist by James Lenox, New York; New York Public Library (Lenox collection); M. Knoedler and Company, New York (1945)
Exhibited: New York, Goupil's Gallery, spring 1863; London, McLean's Gallery, 1865; New York, Museum of Modern Art, "Romantic Painting in America," Nov. 15, 1943–Feb. 6, 1944 (no. 49, reprod.); Memphis, Brooks Memorial Art Gallery, "A Loan Exhibition of American Paintings," Oct. 5–29, 1945 (no. 23)
Lent by Mr. John Astor, New York

This work, resulting from Church's 1857 trip to South America, is more a statement of the phenomenons of nature and less an exercise in topography than was the version of 1855. Another rendering of the subject is in the Art Institute of Chicago.

83. "CHIMBORAZO"

Oil on canvas, 48 x 84 in.

Signed and dated 1864
Collection: commissioned by William Henry Osborn, New York; William Church Osborn (his son); Frederick Osborn (his son)
Exhibited: London, McLean's Gallery, 1865; Philadelphia, American Centennial Exhibition, 1876 (no. 440); New York, Metropolitan Museum of Art, "Paintings by Frederic E. Church, N.A.," May 28–Oct. 15, 1900 (reprod.); Detroit, Detroit Institute of Arts, "The World of the Romantic Artist," Dec. 28, 1944–Jan. 28, 1945 (no. 65, as "Cimborasso" and erroneously dated "about 1875"); Chicago, Art Institute of Chicago, and New York, Whitney Museum of American Art, "The Hudson River School," Feb.–May 1945 (no. 30, reprod.)
Lent by Mr. Frederick Osborn, New York

84. WILDFLOWERS, JAMAICA

Oil on cardboard, 13⅜ x 15¹¹⁄₁₆ in.
Undated (April–Aug. 1865)
Lent by the Cooper Union Museum, New York

85. A BAMBOO GROVE, JAMAICA

Pencil and oil on cardboard, 11⁹⁄₁₆ x 18½ in.
Dated May 1865
Lent by the Cooper Union Museum, New York

86. STUDY OF A COTTON TREE, JAMAICA

Pencil and white gouache on greenish paper, 17⅜ x 10¾ in.

92. Scene in the Blue Mountains, Jamaica (photo courtesy of the Frick Art Reference Library)

Dated May 1865
Lent by the Cooper Union Museum, New York

87. STUDY OF A LIZARD, JAMAICA

Oil on heavy paper, 12 x 6¼ in.
Dated June 1865
Lent by the Cooper Union Museum, New York

88. TROPICAL RAIN FOREST, JAMAICA

Pencil and oil on cardboard, 11⅞ x 19⅞ in.
Dated August 1865
Lent by the Cooper Union Museum, New York

89. VIEW OF THE PALISADOS FROM WARWICK HILL, NEAR KINGSTON, JAMAICA

Pencil and oil on cardboard, 10¼ x 12 in.
Undated (probably August 1865)
Lent by the Cooper Union Museum, New York

90. SCENE IN THE BLUE MOUNTAINS, JAMAICA

Oil on cardboard, 9¼ x 14½ in.
Undated (probably August 1865)
Lent by the Cooper Union Museum, New York

91. IN THE BLUE MOUNTAINS, JAMAICA

Pencil and oil on cardboard, 11½ x 17⅞ in.
Dated August 1865
Lent by the Cooper Union Museum, New York

Church identifies a similar pencil study (Cooper Union Museum) as "Near Galloway Hill."

92. SCENE IN THE BLUE MOUNTAINS, JAMAICA

Oil on cardboard, 11 x 18 in.
Dated August 1865
Collection: Olana
Lent by Olana Preservation, Inc.

93. STUDY FOR "RAINY SEASON IN THE TROPICS"

Pencil on white, lined paper, $5\frac{3}{16}$ x 8⅛ in.
Undated (about 1865–66)
Lent by the Cooper Union Museum, New York

This drawing is a rare instance in Church's oeuvre when the artist has left a rapid sketch for a major painting. On the reverse side of the sheet are brief sketches, designs for a house, possibly referring to improvements of The Farm at Hudson.

94. "RAINY SEASON IN THE TROPICS"

Oil on canvas, 55 x 84 in.
Signed and dated 1866

Collection: painted for Marshall O. Roberts, New York; Jonathan Sturges; H. C. Sturges (his son) and descendants (to 1965)

Exhibited: Paris, Exposition Universelle, 1867; New York, National Academy of Design, 1868; New York, Metropolitan Museum of Art, "Paintings by Frederic E. Church, N.A.," May 28–Oct. 15, 1900 (reprod.); ibid., "Three Centuries of American Art," April–Oct. 1965

Lent by Mr. and Mrs. J. William Middendorf, II, New York

95. *The Vale of St. Thomas, Jamaica*

95. "THE VALE OF ST. THOMAS, JAMAICA"

Oil on canvas, 48$\frac{5}{16}$ x 85⅝ in.
Signed and dated 1867

Collection: painted for Elizabeth Hart (Mrs. Samuel) Colt, Hartford; bequeathed by her to the museum, 1905

Exhibited: New York, Goupil's Gallery, about 1871; New York, Metropolitan Museum of Art, "Paintings by Frederic E. Church, N.A.," May 28–Oct. 15, 1900 (reprod.); Hartford, Wadsworth Atheneum, "A Second Look: Late 19th-Century Taste in Painting," July 8–Aug. 6, 1958 (no. 48)

Lent by the Wadsworth Atheneum, Hartford, Conn. (Bequest of Mrs. Samuel Colt)

This is the one important painting which resulted from the artist's Jamaican sojourn.

96. TROPICAL SCENERY

Oil on canvas, 38⅜ x 59⅞ in.
Signed and dated 1873

Collection: Robert Hoe (sold, New York, American Art Association, Feb. 28, 1882, for $3175); Roderick Terry (sold, Newport, R. I., Gustave J. S. White, Inc.); Vose Galleries, Boston; museum purchase, 1963

Lent by the Brooklyn Museum, Brooklyn, N. Y.

Here Church puts into practical application a knowledge of Ruskin's precepts of landscape painting (as set forth through the work of J. M. W. Turner), in which are synthesized the tropics of South America within a single composition.

97. "MORNING IN THE TROPICS"

Oil on canvas, 54 x 84 in.
Signed and dated 1877

Collection: painted for William Earl Dodge, Riverdale, N. Y.; William Earl Dodge, Jr., Old Westbury, N. Y.; Mrs. Ryan (his daughter); Preservation Society of Newport County, Newport, R. I. (gift of Mrs. Ryan) (to 1965)

Exhibited: Paris, Exposition Universelle, 1878; New York, Century Association, 1879; New York, Metropolitan Museum of Art, "Paintings by Frederic E. Church, N.A.," May 28–Oct. 15, 1900 (reprod.)

Lent by the National Gallery of Art, Washington, D. C. (gift of the Avalon Foundation) (Washington showing only)

THE FAR NORTH

98. THREE STUDIES OF ICEBERGS, NEWFOUNDLAND

Oil on cardboard, 5$\frac{1}{16}$ x 11⅛ in. (average size)
Dated June 1859
Lent by the Cooper Union Museum, New York

99. SHIPS NEAR NEWFOUNDLAND

Pencil and oil on cardboard, 9⅛ x 12⅞ in.
Undated (June-July 1859)
Lent by the Cooper Union Museum, New York

101. Icebergs near Cape St. John and Gull Island

The larger ship is probably the *Merlin*, in which Church and Louis Noble traveled north, and which the latter describes as "a small propeller, with a screw wheel, and a crazy mess of machinery in the middle, which go far toward making one deaf by day, but very wakeful and talkative by night."

100. FLOATING ICEBERG

Oil on cardboard, $12\frac{1}{16}$ x $20\frac{1}{8}$ in.
Undated (July 1859)
Lent by the Cooper Union Museum, New York

101. ICEBERGS NEAR CAPE ST. JOHN AND GULL ISLAND, NEWFOUNDLAND

Pencil and white gouache on grey paper, $10\frac{13}{16}$ x $17\frac{7}{8}$ in.
Dated July 4, 1859
Lent by the Cooper Union Museum, New York

Noble writes: "Cape St. John!—It is terribly awful and impressive—The wind is cold and bracing, sweeping alike the sea and the sky of fog and clouds, and driving us to heavy winter clothing. As we bear down the Cape, we pass Gull Isle a mere pile of naked rocks delicately wreathed with lace-like mists—painting, sketching, and pencilling as we go."

102. THREE SKETCHES: THE SEA AND ICEBERGS, NEW-FOUNDLAND

Pencil and white gouache on light brown paper, $4\frac{1}{2}$ x $8\frac{3}{16}$ in. (each)

Dated June 21 and July 6, 1859
Lent by the Cooper Union Museum, New York

103. STUDIES OF FLOATING ICEBERGS

Pencil and oil on cardboard, 12 x $18\frac{1}{8}$ in.
Dated July 4, 1859
Lent by the Cooper Union Museum, New York

104. "THE ICEBERGS" (also known as "THE NORTH")

Chromolithograph, 21 x $35\frac{3}{4}$ in. (picture area)
Collection: Olana
Lent by Olana Preservation, Inc.

The painting, dated 1861 and now lost, was considered Church's most important Northern subject. It was exhibited first in New York, and then in London. From there it entered an English private collection and has not been heard of since. The chromolithograph was published by C. Risdon in London in 1863.

105. TWO ICEBERG FANTASIES

Oil on cardboard, $5\frac{1}{2}$ x $6\frac{7}{8}$ and $6\frac{3}{8}$ x $10\frac{5}{16}$ in.
Undated (July 1859)
Lent by the Cooper Union Museum, New York

These studies seem to fit Noble's description of the icebergs off Cape St. John. He says: "Of all objects an iceberg is in the highest degree multiform in its effect. Changeable in its colors as the streamers of the northern sky, it will also pass from one shape to another with singular rapidity. As we recede, the upper portions of the solid ice have a light and aerial effect, a description of which is simply impossible. Peaks and spires rise out of strong and apparently unchanging base with the light activity of flame. A mighty structure on fire, all in ice!"

106. THREE SKETCHES OF AN AURORA BOREALIS OVER
MOUNT DESERT ISLAND, MAINE

Pencil on white paper, $4\frac{5}{16}$ x $7\frac{3}{16}$ in. (each)
Dated September 1860
Lent by the Cooper Union Museum, New York

These sketches positively identify the locale which inspired "The Aurora Borealis."

107. STUDY OF AN AURORA BOREALIS, MOUNT DESERT
ISLAND, MAINE

Oil on cardboard, $10\frac{5}{16}$ x $13\frac{7}{8}$ in.
Undated (September 1860)
Lent by the Cooper Union Museum, New York

108. "THE AURORA BOREALIS"

Oil on canvas, 56 x 83 in.
Signed and dated 1865

Collection: commissioned by William T. Blodgett, New York (died 1900); Miss Eleanor Blodgett (his daughter), who presented it to the Smithsonian Institution, 1911.

Exhibited: London, McLean's Gallery, 1865; New York, Metropolitan Museum of Art, "Paintings by Frederic E. Church, N.A.," May 28–Oct. 15, 1900 (reprod.); Richmond, Virginia Museum of Fine Arts,

"Inaugural Exhibition—Main Currents in the Development of American Painting," Jan. 16–March 1, 1936 (no. 48)

Lent by the National Collection of Fine Arts, Smithsonian Institution, Washington, D. C.

Although the idea of the aurora borealis and the hill mass in the foreground are based on Church's sketches made at Mount Desert Island in 1860, the artist has conceived his work in a setting of the Far North. The distant pyramidal peak is based on a chalk sketch by Dr. Isaac Hayes of Church's Peak, Labrador, named for the artist. It is of interest to note that both Church and Blodgett appear on the list of subscribers to Dr. Hayes' expedition on the schooner *United States* to the Arctic.

109. "THE ICEBERG"

Oil on canvas, 20 x 30 in.
Signed and dated 1891

Collection: given by the artist to his son, Theodore Winthrop Church; Mrs. Theodore W. Church (aunt of the present owner)

Exhibited: Brooklyn, Brooklyn Museum, "The Coast and The Sea," Nov. 19, 1948–Jan. 16, 1949 (no. 29, reprod., p. 24); Northampton, Smith College Museum of Art, "An Exhibition of American Painting for a Professor of American Art," May 14–June 14, 1964 (no. 14)

Lent by Miss Frances Sauvalle, Galveston, Texas

Still painting icebergs in the very last decade of his [71] life, Church continues to show the magnitude of these natural forms in the cold light of the far North.

THE OLD WORLD

110. SKETCH OF JAFFA, WITH A PARADE IN THE FORE-
GROUND

Pencil and oil on cardboard, 13 x 20$\frac{1}{16}$ in.
Lent by the Cooper Union Museum, New York

Church visited Jaffa first on February 7 and again exactly a month later, in 1868.

111. SKETCHES OF JERUSALEM IN MOONLIGHT; SILOAM,
PALESTINE

Pencil and white gouache on grey paper, 4$\frac{13}{16}$ x 8$\frac{1}{8}$, 7 x 9$\frac{13}{16}$, and 4$\frac{13}{16}$ x 8$\frac{9}{16}$ in.
Sketches of Jerusalem dated April 2, 1868; view of Siloam dated February 7, 1868

Lent by the Cooper Union Museum, New York

The lower sketch shows the city from the Mount of Olives. The Dome of the Rock is seen in both views.

112. VIEW OF EL KHASNÉ, PETRA

Pencil and oil on cardboard, 12$\frac{7}{8}$ x 20$\frac{1}{8}$ in.
Executed between February 20 and 27, 1868
Lent by the Cooper Union Museum, New York

113. STUDY OF ROCKS, PETRA, SYRIA

[72]   Pencil and oil on cardboard, 12 x 20$\frac{1}{8}$ in.

Executed between February 20 and 27, 1868
Lent by the Cooper Union Museum, New York

114. VIEW OF WADI-EL-ARABAH, ARABIA

Pencil and white gouache on greenish paper, 10$\frac{3}{4}$ x 17$\frac{1}{4}$ in.
Dated February 21, 1868
Lent by the Cooper Union Museum, New York

This scene is in the neighborhood of Petra.

115. JERUSALEM FROM THE MOUNT OF OLIVES

Pencil and oil on cardboard, 11$\frac{13}{16}$ x 18$\frac{1}{2}$ in.
Undated (April 1868)
Lent by the Cooper Union Museum, New York

116. STUDY OF A BEDOUIN

Oil on brown paper, 13$\frac{7}{8}$ x 10$\frac{1}{4}$ in.
Undated (1868)
Lent by the Cooper Union Museum, New York

117. ARAB COSTUME SKETCH

Pencil and white gouache on grey paper, 10$\frac{3}{4}$ x 7$\frac{5}{8}$ in.
Undated (1868)
Lent by the Cooper Union Museum, New York

Always interested in representing exactness of detail in his work, Church brought back with him from his trip to the Near East a number of Arab costumes, from which he painted the figures in the "Jerusalem."

118. A CROUCHING DROMEDARY

Pencil and oil on cardboard, $11\frac{13}{16}$ x $18\frac{1}{2}$ in.
Lent by the Cooper Union Museum, New York
Undated, this sketch was executed during the artist's
sojourn in the Near East from January to May 1868.

119. SKETCH OF THE PRAETORIUM IN MUSMIYEH,
PHAENAE, SYRIA

Pencil and white gouache on grey paper, $11\frac{3}{4}$ x $17\frac{5}{8}$
in.
Undated (April 28, 1868)
Lent by the Cooper Union Museum, New York

120. FALLEN FRAGMENTS FROM THE INTERIOR OF THE
TEMPLE OF BACCHUS, AT BAALBEK, SYRIA

Pencil and oil on cardboard, 10 x $11\frac{1}{4}$ in.
Undated (May 1868)
Lent by the Cooper Union Museum, New York

Although the classical architecture of Rome had little
appeal to Church, he was fascinated by that which he
encountered in the Near East.

121. CONSTANTINOPLE BY MOONLIGHT, FROM THE
GENOESE TOWER

Pencil and white gouache on greenish paper, $11\frac{7}{8}$ x
$17\frac{7}{16}$ in.
Dated June 4, 1868
Lent by the Cooper Union Museum, New York

In the middle distance appears the Golden Horn,
with the Bosporus and Sea of Marmara in the far distance.

122. THE KOENIGSEE, NEAR BERCHTESGADEN, BAVARIA

Pencil and oil on cardboard, $11\frac{3}{8}$ x $11\frac{7}{8}$ in.
Undated (June–July 1868)
Lent by the Cooper Union Museum, New York

123. THREE SKETCHES OF THE KOENIGSEE, NEAR BERCH-
TESGADEN, BAVARIA

Pencil and white gouache on greyish paper, $8\frac{1}{16}$ x $4\frac{3}{4}$
in. (each)
Dated July 1868
Lent by the Cooper Union Museum, New York

These sketches all come from the same pocket sketchbook. It was Church's habit to dismember his sketchbooks so as to be able to shuffle the sketches and
larger drawings together in the process of composing a final painting. Because of this, no sketchbook
by him has survived intact.

124. TWO SCENES NEAR BERCHTESGADEN, BAVARIA: A
WAYSIDE SHRINE AND A FARMHOUSE

Pencil and oil on cardboard, 7 x $4\frac{1}{2}$ and $4\frac{1}{2}$ x 9 in.
Dated July 1868
Lent by the Cooper Union Museum, New York

125. THE CASTLE AT SALZBURG, AUSTRIA, AS SEEN FROM
THE WEST

Pencil and oil on cardboard, $12\frac{3}{4}$ x $19\frac{3}{4}$ in.
Undated (July 8, 1868)

116. Study of a Bedouin

119. Sketch of the Praetorium

Lent by the Cooper Union Museum, New York

The only recorded visit to Salzburg by Church was a side trip from Berchtesgaden, some ten miles distant. The results of this excursion include four oil sketches and perhaps a half dozen or so pencil drawings and sketches, giving some idea of Church's artistic production on a single day.

126. STUDY OF TREE ROOTS
Pencil and white gouache on cream-colored paper, $10\frac{3}{4}$ x $17\frac{1}{4}$ in.
Dated July 16, 1868
Lent by the Cooper Union Museum, New York

The locale on the sketch is identified as the Koenigsee, near Berchtesgaden, Bavaria.

127. THE OBERSEE, BAVARIA
Pencil and white gouache on greenish paper, $11\frac{7}{8}$ x $17\frac{1}{2}$ in.
Dated July 17, 1868
Lent by the Cooper Union Museum, New York

128. TWO PANORAMIC VIEWS OF THE UPPER ALETSCH GLACIER, IN THE BERNESE ALPS, FROM BEL ALP, SWITZERLAND
Pencil and white gouache on cream-colored and grey paper, $11\frac{7}{8}$ x $26\frac{1}{2}$ in. (each)
Dated August 27 and 28, 1868
Lent by the Cooper Union Museum, New York

129. LITTLE CHURCH NEAR BEL ALP, BERNESE ALPS, SWITZERLAND
Pencil and white gouache on brown paper, $8\frac{3}{4}$ x $11\frac{1}{8}$ in.
Dated August 28, 1868
Lent by the Cooper Union Museum, New York

130. TWO SKETCHES FROM THE VALAIS, SWITZERLAND
Pencil and white gouache on brown paper, $8\frac{3}{4}$ x $4\frac{13}{16}$ and $4\frac{3}{4}$ x $8\frac{1}{8}$ in.
Dated August 1868
Lent by the Cooper Union Museum, New York

131. THREE VIEWS OF ROME: from the villa of Claude Lorrain with the Castel Sant' Angelo and Saint Peter's in the distance, and from the Pincio
Pencil and oil on cardboard, $4\frac{1}{2}$ x $8\frac{7}{8}$ in. (each)
Undated (winter 1868–69)
Lent by the Cooper Union Museum, New York

While in Rome Church's chief artistic concern was with the effects of light and atmosphere. As for the city itself, he found "the subjects as threadbare as the priests," and to him the "gross architecture looked cheap and vulgar."

132. THREE SKETCHES OF THE PARTHENON, ATHENS
Pencil on grey and green paper, $4\frac{3}{16}$ x 8 in. (each)
Undated (April 1869)
Lent by the Cooper Union Museum, New York

129. Little Church near Bel Alp

These constitute the first sketches for the painting "The Parthenon" (Metropolitan Museum of Art, New York; not included in the exhibition), completed in 1871.

133. VIEW OF THE NORTH PERISTYLE OF THE PARTHE-
NON, ATHENS

Pencil and oil on cardboard, 13 x 10 in.
Undated (April 1869)
Lent by the Cooper Union Museum, New York

Church did seven other oil studies of the Parthenon, including one at night in the light of flares. One of these is dated April 21, 1869.

134. SCULPTURED SOCLE IN THE THEATRE OF DIONYSUS,
ATHENS

Pencil and oil on cardboard, $10\frac{1}{16}$ x 13 in.
Undated (April 1869)
Lent by the Cooper Union Museum, New York

In speaking of the impression made upon him by the Acropolis, Church remarked that "No photograph can convey even a faint impression of its [the Parthenon's] majesty and beauty. Fragments of sculpture are strewn all about. The Greeks had noble conceptions. They gave a large God-like air to all they did and the fragments and bits are full of merit."

135. LANDSCAPE IN GREECE (DELPHI?)

Oil on paper, 13 x 20⅛ in.
Undated (1869?)

Lent by the Cooper Union Museum, New York

It is difficult to determine whether this work is an intended fantasy or derives from an actual scene. Usually Church was exact in his landscape studies, but this scene, though reminiscent of the setting of Delphi, is more imaginary than real.

136. STUDY FOR "JERUSALEM"

Oil on canvas, 9¾ x 15¾ in.
Unsigned (about 1871)

Collection: purchased from the artist by Jonathan Sturges, New York (great-grandfather of the present owner); William Henry Osborn; William Church Osborn (his son)

Lent by Frederick Osborn, New York

This work has never been exhibited or published before.

137. "JERUSALEM"

Oil on canvas, 54 x 84 in.
Signed and dated 1870.

Collection: painted for Thomas Allyn, Hartford, Conn.; Mrs. Harold Ransom, Hartford (died 1965)
Exhibited: New York, Goupil's Gallery, April 1871

Lent by the Estate of Mrs. Harold Ransom

"Jerusalem" received tremendous acclaim from the press at its first public showing, and in Church's obituary (in the Hartford *Courant*, April 9, 1900) it is quoted by the artist as his finest work.

135. Landscape in Greece (Delphi?)

138. "EL KHASNÉ, PETRA"

Oil on canvas, 58 x 46 in.
Signed and dated 1874

Collection: painted as a gift to the artist's wife; Olana

Exhibited: New York, National Academy of Design, 1874 (no. 320); Chicago, Chicago Academy of Design, spring exhibition, 1875; New York, Metropolitan Museum of Art, "Paintings by Frederic E. Church, N.A.," May 28–Oct. 15, 1900 (reprod.)

Lent by Olana Preservation, Inc.

The New York *Daily Tribune* (April 25, 1874) commented of this work that it represented "one of [Church's] least pleasing moods" and that even "a great reputation" could not "save his 'Petra' from the charge of being only a theatrical make-up of the same." Actually, the subject is represented with remarkable accuracy as to its setting, the color of the natural rock formations, and the effects of light upon the architecture.

139. "THE AEGEAN SEA"

Oil on canvas, 54 x 84¼ in.
Signed but not dated (about 1877)

Collection: painted for William H. Osborn; Mrs. William H. Osborn

Exhibited: New York, Goupil's Gallery, April 1878; London, American Fine Arts Society, 1893 (no. 6); New York, Metropolitan Museum of Art, "Paintings by Frederic E. Church, N.A.," May 28–Oct. 15, 1900

Lent by the Metropolitan Museum of Art, New York (Bequest of Mrs. William H. Osborn, 1902)

Vignettes of all the Near East have here been brought together into a single composition: Fallen Monoliths of Baalbeck, a rock temple of Petra, Cape Sounion in Greece, Constantinople, the Bosphorus, and the ruins of Delphi.

140. "THE MONASTERY OF OUR LADY OF THE SNOWS"

Oil on canvas, 46¾ x 72⅛ in.
Signed and dated 1879

Collection: Hinman B. Hurlbut, Cleveland (probably purchased directly from the artist); entered the Cleveland Museum of Art with the Hurlbut collection, 1916

Exhibited: New York, the Century Association, June 1879 (entitled "The Monastery of San Pedro")

Lent by the Cleveland Museum of Art, Cleveland, Ohio (Hinman B. Hurlbut Collection)

141. "THE MEDITERRANEAN SEA"

Oil on canvas, 15 x 22 in.
Signed and dated 1882

Collection: Thomas B. Clarke, New York (sold, New York, American Art Galleries, 1899, no. 87); Mrs. George H. Lewis, New York; Zickel, New York (1944); (sold, Plaza Galleries, New York, Feb. 1953); Robert Manning, New York; Wickersham Gallery, New York

143. *Moses Viewing the Promised Land*

Exhibited: Philadelphia, Pennsylvania Academy of the Fine Arts, "The Clarke Collection," 1891 (p. 29, no. 38)

Lent by Mrs. Iola S. Haverstick, New York

IMAGINARY SUBJECTS

142. "HOOKER AND COMPANY JOURNEYING THROUGH THE WILDERNESS FROM PLYMOUTH TO HARTFORD IN 1636"

Oil on canvas, 39¼ x 59½ in.
Signed and dated 1846

Collection: purchased by the Wadsworth Atheneum directly from the artist in 1846 (for $130), constituting the first documented sale of a painting by Church

Exhibited: New York, National Academy of Design, 1846 (no. 114); American Federation of Arts traveling exhibition, "19th-Century American Paintings Exhibition for Germany," 1953–54

Lent by the Wadsworth Atheneum, Hartford, Conn.

In a letter to his teacher, Cole, dated Oct. 17, 1846, Church says: "Some of the gentlemen connected with the Wadsworth Gallery are trying to purchase my Hooker picture. This I have improved by glazing, etc. —." The scene depicts a peaceful event that began a new American era. On May 31, 1636, the Reverend Thomas Hooker, of Newtown (now Cambridge), Massachusetts, with a small party, set forth and traveled two weeks through the forests to the Connecticut River. There they founded Hartford,

soon to become the first sizable inland settlement in Connecticut. This move constituted the first stage in the great migration to the West.

This work is one of few examples in which Church introduced a subject into otherwise pure landscape painting.

143. "MOSES VIEWING THE PROMISED LAND"

Oil on academy board, 9⅝ x 12½ in.
Signed and dated 1846

Collection: Thomas Cole (and his descendants); Mrs. Florence Cole Vincent (1954); Robert G. McIntyre (trade) (as a sketch by Cole)

Lent anonymously

144. "CHRISTIAN ON THE BORDERS OF THE 'VALLEY OF THE SHADOW OF DEATH,' *Pilgrim's Progress*"

Oil on canvas, 40 x 60 in.
Unsigned (about 1847)
Collection: Olana

Exhibited: New York, National Academy of Design, 1847 (no. 84)

Lent by Olana Preservation, Inc.

The exhibition of this work brought the first notice given to Church by a critic, when the *Literary World* (vol. 1, May 22, 1847, p. 371) remarked that the picture was by a "promising young artist, who is or has been a pupil of Cole's," and that "time and experience will enable him to take rank with our best landscape painters."

149. Vision of the Cross

The subject, taken from Bunyan's *Pilgrim's Progress*, is an excuse for the artist to inject an almost supernatural mood into the landscape.

145. COTTAGE NEAR A BODY OF WATER

Pencil, white gouache, and watercolors on prepared paper (mounted), $5\frac{1}{16}$ x 8⅛ in.
Undated (about 1855–60)
Collection: Cyrus W. Field; Isabella Field (Mrs. William Francis) Judson; Cyrus Field Judson (her son)
Lent by Mrs. Alice Judson Jones, Washington, D. C.

Probably a presentation piece by the artist to his friend Field. Finished drawings of this type are uncommon with Church, but occasionally he executed them to distribute among his close friends.

146. "OUR BANNER IN THE SKY"

Chromolithograph, 7⅜ x 11¼ in. (picture area)
Collection: Olana
Lent by Olana Preservation, Inc.

The painting by this title, now lost, was exhibited at Goupil's Gallery, New York, in 1861. In an unidentified newspaper article it is stated that the work "was 'chromoed' extensively during the Civil War and well known throughout the country." Today, however, as is the case with other prints after Church's paintings, this item is extremely rare.

147. "MOONRISE" (memorial to the artist's recently deceased children)

Oil on canvas, 10 x 13½ in.
Signed and dated 1865
Collection: Olana
Lent by Olana Preservation, Inc.

This and the following work are tokens of the tragedy that befell the artist when, in March 1865, his two small children died of diphtheria almost within a week of one another.

148. "SUNRISE" (memorial to the artist's recently deceased children)

Oil on canvas, 10 x 13½ in.
Unsigned (1865)
Collection: Olana
Lent by Olana Preservation, Inc.

149. VISION OF THE CROSS

Pencil and white opaque watercolor on cream-colored paper, 11⅞ x 17½ in.
Lent by the Cooper Union Museum, New York

This drawing (probably executed in September 1868 as indicated by other dated drawings on the same kind of paper) and the two following oil sketches doubtless reflect "The Cross of the World," Cole's last large series, left unfinished at his death. The last picture in the series, entitled "The Vision," must have constituted the initial inspiration for Church's composition.

150. TWO STUDIES OF THE VISION OF THE CROSS

Oil on paper, 7¼ x 10⅛, and 8½ x $12\frac{13}{16}$ in.

Undated (about 1868)
Lent by the Cooper Union Museum, New York

151. CHARIOT OF THE MOON

Oil on cardboard, 12⅞ x 11 9/16 in.
Lent by the Cooper Union Museum, New York

In a Hudson Valley setting the chariot of a harvest moon, driven by a phantasmagorical figure, dashes through the sky above an enigmatic gibbet. Stylistically this work would seem to belong in the late 1860's.

152. TWO IMAGINARY LANDSCAPE STUDIES

Pen and brown ink on paper, 4½ x 6⅞ and 5 1/16 x 6⅝ in.
Lent by the Cooper Union Museum, New York

A late dating in the artist's career is indicated by the freedom with which these sketches have been made. In them recollections of South America and Europe are deftly combined.

153. TWELVE LANDSCAPE COMPOSITIONS, SOME SHOW-ING A CASTLE ON A PROMONTORY

Pencil, pen, and brown ink with ink wash on paper, 3½ x 4½ in. (average size)
Undated (about 1880–90)
Lent by the Cooper Union Museum, New York

The motif of a circular castle keep on a promontory appears in Church's late paintings (e.g. "The Mediterranean" and "Constantinople") but this would not preclude dating these drawings somewhat earlier.

154. RUINED CASTLE IN A TROPICAL SETTING

Oil on academy board, 6⅜ x 9¼ in.
Lent by the Cooper Union Museum, New York

Even though this sketch could date as late as the 1870's, Church indicates still the presence of Cole in his thoughts.

155. SHEET OF SKETCHES OF GROTESQUE FIGURES

Pencil on cream-colored paper, 9⅜ x 4 13/16 in.
Lent by the Cooper Union Museum, New York

This sheet is an indication of Church's sense of humor and what was to be perceived in nature.

156. "THE LETTER REVENGE"

Oil on canvas, 8¼ x 10¼ in.
Unsigned (about 1847)

Collection: Charles F. Olney, Cleveland (gift by him to the museum, 1904)

Exhibited: Oberlin, Allen Memorial Art Museum, Oberlin College, "Still Life Paintings 17th to 19th Century," March 1945; ibid., "American Painters Discover America," Feb. 1946

Lent by the Allen Memorial Art Museum, Oberlin College, Oberlin, Ohio

Being so untypical a subject with Church, it is questionable as to whether or not the work is by him, or whether, perhaps, it represents a jibe directed at Church by another artist. In any case, no similar work by Church is known.

155. Sheet of Sketches of Grotesque Figures